INSTITUTE OF GEC

GEOLOGICAL SURV

The Geology of the Church Stretton area

(Explanation of 1:25 000 Geological Sheet SO49)

J. E. WRIGHT, B.Sc.

LONDON
HER MAJESTY'S STATIONERY OFFICE
1968

First published 1968
Second impression 1969
Third impression 1983

ISBN 0 11 880082 5

PREFACE

The 1:25 000 sheet of the Church Stretton area is the first geological map at this scale to be published by the Institute of Geological Sciences. It shows all the topographical detail available on the larger six inches to one mile maps, at which scale the area was surveyed, and it carries contours at 25-ft intervals. In complicated areas details of the geology can be usually delineated without the generalization sometimes necessary on the one inch to one mile map.

This account of the geology is designed to be read in conjunction with the map, so that the reader is referred to the vertical sections at the side of the map for a statement of the geological succession, and extensive use has been made of the National Grid, printed on the map, in defining the positions of exposures and other localities.

The Church Stretton area contains an impressive variety of rocks and has been the scene of classic geological research since the early part of the 19th century. Its geology and rural beauty make it an ideal centre for geological excursions and it is hoped that the new map and its description will prove useful to many geologists, both amateur and professional.

K. C. DUNHAM
Director

Institute of Geological Sciences
Geological Survey Office
Exhibition Road
South Kensington
LONDON SW7
3rd August 1967

CONTENTS

LIST OF TEXT FIGURES

1/INTRODUCTION

The area shown on 1:25 000 geological sheet SO49 is centred
on the small town of Church Stretton, in the borderland
hill country of south Shropshire. The ground is divided from
N.E. to S.W. by the Church Stretton valley which carries
the railway line between Ludlow and Shrewsbury, and also
the line of the main road along an old Roman route leading
to the settlement of Uriconium near Shrewsbury. At Church
Stretton there is a watershed in the valley bottom at about
620 ft O.D., dividing streams which flow northwards to the
River Severn from the southward drainage of tributaries
of the River Teme. The valley is bounded to the W. by the
Long Mynd plateau which reaches 1695 ft O.D. at Pole
Bank [41529444][1] and which carries an ancient trackway,
the Port Way, to the N. and S. of the summit. South of
Stanbatch [405938] the plateau is limited to the W. by a
steep scarp about 400 ft high and trending almost N.–S.
along the line of the Long Mynd Scarp Fault. This steep
slope and the prevailing westerly winds create conditions
favourable to the activities of the Midland Gliding Club
with its headquarters situated near the Port Way [40329152]
at the top of the scarp. The eastern part of the Long Mynd
is deeply dissected by a series of narrow valleys, locally
known as batches, draining south-eastwards to the Church
Stretton valley and well known to many visitors to the district.
To the E. the valley is dominated by a line of narrow hills
from Ragleth Hill [455921] in the S. to The Lawley [495975]
in the N., reaching a maximum height of 1500 ft O.D. in
Caer Caradoc Hill, crowned by the ramparts of an Iron
Age camp. This line of hills is composed mainly of Uriconian
rocks the outcrops of which are bounded largely by the
component faults of the Church Stretton Complex but

---

[1] Such numbers are National Grid references within the 100-km square SO

which also occur N.E. of Hope Bowdler [475925] in Hope Bowdler, Willstone and Cardington hills. The 'vale and edge' topography of the ground S. of Hope Bowdler and E. of Comley [485965] reflects the easterly dip of Ordovician beds of different hardness which crop out in these areas. The low, drift-covered ground between Leebotwood [476988] and The Lawley is underlain by shales with thin coal seams of Upper Carboniferous age which were worked in small collieries up to about 1876. Remains of the old pits can be seen N. of Leebotwood [477999] and near Botvyle [47469650].

Geological History

The succession of rocks occurring in the area is shown in the vertical sections on either side of the map. The solid rocks range in age from Pre-Cambrian (at least 700 million years old) to Upper Coal Measures (about 295 million years old) and they are covered locally by a variety of drift deposits, the bulk of which were probably laid down during and after the Glacial Period (i.e. since about 1 million years ago). Some of the rock groups are separated by unconformities which represent periods of time during which folding and erosion took place before the deposition of the succeeding sediments.

The oldest rocks are the Uriconian tuffs and lavas of the Ragleth–Lawley–Cardington hills and their extrusion was succeeded by the deposition of the Longmyndian sediments which occupy all the area W. of the Church Stretton valley. The Longmyndian was probably deposited in a fault-bounded trough of no great depth since many of the shales and sandstones of the Stretton Series exhibit shallow-water features and some of the conglomerates and coarse sandstones of the Wentnor Series are probably of similar origin. Strong folding and denudation preceded the deposition of the Cambrian sediments which crop out in the Comley area [485960]. The basal beds are quartzites, laid down in a shallow current-swept sea, succeeded by shallow-water glauconitic sandstones. These Lower Cambrian beds were folded and differentially eroded before the deposition of Middle Cambrian shales and sandstones. Steady subsidence followed in Upper Cambrian times with the deposition of a considerable thickness of mudstones, and the Cambrian Period was terminated by widespread uplift with some minor folding.

During Ordovician and Silurian times, sedimentation in the Church Stretton area took place in the relatively shallow seas of the Midland shelf area which can be contrasted with the more rapidly subsiding Welsh geosynclinal basin to the W. Although a complete lower Ordovician sequence occurs in the Shelve area W. of the Long Mynd, the Ordovician is represented in the Church Stretton area only by the Caradoc Series, of upper Ordovician age, consisting of shallow-water sandstones and siltstones with an abundant shelly fauna. A landscape of considerable relief was developed by uplift and folding at the end of the Ordovician Period and in Upper Llandovery times a marine transgression from the Welsh basin resulted in the deposition of grits and conglomerates on the S.E. margin of the Long Mynd. These rocks, which crop out S.W. of Little Stretton [443929] are succeeded and overlapped by the shallow-water limestones and siltstones of the *Pentamerus* Beds and the mudstones of the Hughley Shales. During Wenlock and Ludlow times the boundary between the geosynclinal deposition in the W. and shallower shelf deposition in the E., seems to have been close to the line of the Church Stretton Fault Complex. The Wenlock and Ludlow rocks of the Church Stretton valley are limestones, calcareous siltstones and mudstones of shallow-water type similar to the rocks of the Wenlock and Aymestry scarps to the S.E. Rocks of the geosynclinal facies occur W. of the Long Mynd beyond the area of the map.

Old Red Sandstone rocks do not occur in the Church Stretton area although there are extensive outcrops not far away to the S.E. around the Clee hills. The Carboniferous system is represented only by the Coed-yr-Allt Beds of Upper Coal Measures age, in the Leebotwood Coalfield. These rocks are shales, sandstones and thin coals which were the result of the rhythmic deltaic sedimentation which characterized much of the deposition of the Coal Measures in other parts of Britain.

There is a gap in the local sedimentary record between the Coed-yr-Allt Beds (about 295 million years old) and the drift deposits of Pleistocene times (up to about one million years old). During the latter period the Church Stretton area was invaded by ice from the Shropshire Plain to the N. and the Welsh hills to the W. The sequence of the glacial deposits, mainly boulder clay and gravel, indicates only one period of glaciation in which the ice advanced down the Church Stretton valley as far S. as about Marshbrook [442898]. There is no evidence that ice covered the high ground of the Long Mynd and the Uriconian hills. The gravel deposits of the Church Stretton valley, the Hope Bowdler and Leebotwood areas were probably laid down during the northward retreat of the ice in its waning phase.

2/PRE-CAMBRIAN: URICONIAN

Uriconian rocks form a line of narrow hills stretching from Ragleth Hill in the S.W. to The Lawley in the N.E. and also the range of hills N. and N.E. of Hope Bowdler. They are mainly of volcanic origin and include lavas of basaltic, andesitic, dacitic and rhyolitic character together with tuffs (consolidated volcanic ash) and a small development of tuffaceous grit and conglomerate. The Uriconian outcrops are separated by faults or unconformities from younger rocks ranging in age from Longmyndian to Upper Coal Measures. The occurrence of the basal Cambrian quartzite on the N.E. side of Caer Caradoc Hill [480957], resting unconformably on various members of the Uriconian sequence, indicates the Pre-Cambrian age of the latter.

It is not possible to recognize a stratigraphical succession applicable to the whole area. The individual outcrops are generally bounded by faults, the throws of which cannot be precisely determined, so that different portions of the Uriconian sequence in separate fault blocks cannot always be related to each other. The problem is made more acute locally by lack of exposures and by the sheared and altered state of the rocks. It is convenient to describe the Uriconian outcrops under separate areas as follows: 1. The Lawley. 2. Caer Caradoc Hill, Helmeth Hill and Ragleth Hill. 3. Hazler Hill. 4. Hope Bowdler Hill. 5. Cardington Hill.

The Lawley

The Lawley inlier is limited to the E. by the unconformable basal Cambrian quartzite, to the W. by fault F1 of the Church Stretton Complex (Cobbold, 1927 p. 565), and is separated from Little Caradoc [482961] by downfaulted outcrops of Cambrian rocks in the Comley gap. It appears that the regional dip is generally steep to the

E., the strike swinging from N.N.E. in the N. to about N.-S. at the southern end of The Lawley. The correct stratigraphical sequence is uncertain but the probable downward succession in the S. part of the hill is as follows:

Basic Tuffs (probably over 500 ft)
Upper Andesites (probably over 300 ft)
Rhyolite (about 100 ft)
Lower Andesites (more than 500 ft)

The Lower Andesites are badly weathered, close-jointed dark grey rocks commonly with amygdales infilled with quartz or calcite which may weather out to give a scoriaceous appearance. Near the S.W. corner of the hill [48829690] are breccias with limonite-coated fragments, possibly crush breccias.

The overlying rhyolite is a flow-banded amygdaloidal lava which is commonly shattered and jointed and locally broken into an angular crush breccia.

The Upper Andesites are dark grey or purple lavas with amygdales filled by quartz, calcite or yellow radiating epidote. Flow breccias are recognizable by their weathered surfaces and some exposures suggest that the group may consist of thin lavas interbedded with tuffs.

The Basic Tuffs are poorly bedded, fine-grained tuffs containing ragged green or pink rock fragments. They are probably the lowest member of the succession described by Robertson (*in* Pocock and others 1938, p. 28) for the N. part of The Lawley where they are apparently overlain by a sequence of rhyolitic lavas and tuffs.

An outcrop of dolerite, 250 yd wide, extends across The Lawley 400 yd N. of the summit [496979] and another body 400 yd S.W. of the summit [492972] is probably a sill. No dolerites are known to cut the Cambrian, which suggests that they are of Pre-Cambrian age.

Caer Caradoc, Helmeth and Ragleth Hills

The succession in this area is shown on the vertical section of the geological map and the probable structure of the Caer Caradoc area is illustrated in Section 3 below the map. In the N. the Uriconian outcrop is bounded largely by faults F1 and F2 (Cobbold 1927) of the Church Stretton

Complex although on the E. side of Little Caradoc it is unconformably overlain by the basal Cambrian quartzite. S. of Caer Caradoc, the Ragleth Tuffs are overlain to the W. by the basal member of the Longmyndian, the Helmeth Grit. The mapping in the vicinity of Caradoc Coppice [468948] suggests that this junction may be an unconformity, but Cobbold and Whittard (1935, p. 348) concluded that there was transition from the topmost beds of the Ragleth Tuffs into the tuffaceous grits of the Helmeth Grit. The sequence is described as follows in upward order.

COMLEY ANDESITES

These are jointed and weathered, amygdaloidal, dark bluish green rocks, exposed in the side of a lane at [48309644] and in the fields to the N.E.

LITTLE CARADOC TUFFS

The Comley Andesites are overlain by a dolerite body, probably a sill about 500 ft thick, which is succeeded by a thin, well bedded dust tuff, exposed at [48179614] and faulted against Cambrian quartzite to the S. The tuff dips 57° S.W. and minor current bedding indicates that the sequence is right way up. Small outcrops of tuff at [48079596] and [48289600] may belong to this group.

LITTLE CARADOC BASALTS

Albitized basalt lavas overlie the Little Caradoc Tuffs, occupying the N. ridge of Caer Caradoc up to the inner ramparts of the summit camp [47779544], and extending round the E. slope of the hill below the camp. The lowest flows are dark grey fine-grained rocks, similar to those occurring higher up the ridge, but there are also flow-brecciated and amygdaloidal basalts with at least one band of lithic tuff [48089612]. The amygdaloidal rocks are mainly greenish grey or purplish, the amygdales being filled with calcite, chlorite, quartz or hematite.

CAER CARADOC RHYOLITES

The outcrop of the Caer Caradoc Rhyolites extends across the summit of the hill between faults F1 and F2. The rocks include pink or dull red lavas locally with marked flow banding similar to the bedding of fine-grained tuffs, the flow surfaces being marked by lines of elongated amygdales in some instances. Other rock types include breccias with fragments of reddish rhyolite up to about 1 in across, set in a brownish granular matrix. These are thought to be crush breccias but rocks of similar character with fragments up to 6 in across may be flow breccias, for example in the crags on the N. side of the entrance to Caer Caradoc camp [47709516]. The flow banding in the rhyolites is commonly folded intensely and there is a great variety in the amount and direction of plunge of the minor folds. The junction of the group with the overlying Caer Caradoc Andesites is apparently affected by this minor folding but the base of the Caer Caradoc Rhyolites maps out as a plane surface dipping S.W. For this reason it is suggested that the base of the group may be a thrust and an isolated rhyolite crag [47819592] 600 yd N. of Caer Caradoc summit, may be an outlier of the group, separated from the underlying Little Caradoc Basalts by this thrust.

CAER CARADOC ANDESITES

The Caer Caradoc Andesites overlie the Caer Caradoc Rhyolites, the junction apparently being folded. The dip is S.W. and the outcrop extends across Caer Caradoc, S. of the summit, bounded to the S.W. by a normal strike fault which truncates successively higher beds of the Ragleth Tuffs on the W. side of the hill as it is followed westwards. The rocks are mainly dark grey, commonly amygdaloidal and much jointed with thin tuff bands locally. Close to F1 and N. of Three Fingers Rock [47159515] andesites correlated with the Caer Caradoc group are, with the associated Cwms Rhyolites, thrust over the adjoining dolerite to the E.

CWMS RHYOLITES

The junction of the Cwms Rhyolites with the Caer Caradoc Andesites is apparently faulted and is exposed in a gully

[47559488] 550 yd S.S.W. of Caer Caradoc summit. The outcrop is bounded to the S.W. by a faulted junction against the Ragleth Tuffs. West of Three Fingers Rock there are outcrops of sheared and crushed Cwms Rhyolites, thought to be a thrust sheet overlying Ragleth Tuffs. The rhyolites are similar to those of the Caer Caradoc group but tend to be more purplish and green in colour with less conspicuous flow banding. However, amygdales and nodular structures are present, particularly near the base of the group.

RAGLETH TUFFS

The Ragleth Tuffs appear to follow the Cwms Rhyolites conformably and the lowest beds of the group form a syncline (see Section 3 below map), plunging N.W., which gives rise to a narrow U-shaped outcrop across the S. ridge of Caer Caradoc Hill. The core of the fold is occupied by a large dolerite sill with an irregular ramifying junction against the underlying tuffs and enclosing a raft of tuff about 100 yd long. The main outcrop of the Ragleth Tuffs extends from Caradoc Coppice [46829480] to the S. end of Ragleth Hill [445915], being bounded to the S.E. by fault F2 of the Church Stretton Complex and to the N.W. by the base of the Helmeth Grit. At the S. end of Caer Caradoc Hill the dip is mainly steep to the N.E. but there may be repetition of the succession by folding and faulting. The rocks include grit bands with conspicuous pink grains and there are sill-like intrusions of dolerite. The unusual grey colour of some rocks in this area and on Helmeth Hill suggests the presence of rhyolitic flows. On the W. side of Hazler Hill there are outcrops of fine-grained tuffs with intrusive dolerites, associated with considerable development of epidote.

On Ragleth Hill the regional strike is about N.E.–S.W. but the dip is variable. It is uncertain whether there is repetition by folding or faulting, but if the succession is unbroken it must be over 1500 ft thick. The sequence includes pink, brown and purple, fine-grained rhyolitic tuffs locally interbedded with darker, greenish rocks of more sedimentary aspect. In some outcrops bedding is marked by a delicate colour banding and there are traces of current bedding and slump structures with graded bedding in the coarser

9

bands. There are also variable yellowish grits with con-spicuous quartz grains, pink feldspar and pink rhyolite fragments. Cobbold (1900, p. 95) recorded quasi-fossil markings simulating '*Cruziana*' and '*Arenicolites*' from the tuffs. The rocks are much jointed and sheared, locally slickensided and contain crush breccias similar to those in the underlying lavas.

Hazler Hill

The Uriconian rocks of the Hazler Hill area [465925] form a triangular outcrop bounded to the N.W. and N.E. by faults and limited to the S. by an unconformable cover of Harnage Shales. The rocks are mainly albitized, amygda-loidal basaltic lavas, possibly more than 1200 ft thick, locally interbedded with fine-grained tuffs. The most extensive exposures are in and around Hazler Quarry [46289246], celebrated for its Neptunian dykes (Strachan, Temple and Williams 1948, p. 276), and along the lane from Sandford Seat [46809324] to Hazler Barn [46809260]. Sections from these two areas are compared as follows:

Hazler Quarry		Hazler Barn area	
	Thickness in ft		Thickness in ft
Basalt	50	Basalt	100
Tuff	6	Tuff	3
Basalt	2	Grit	unknown
Tuff	11	Tuff	unknown
Basalt	18	Basalt	25
(Dip 50°–80° N.)		Tuff	100
		Basalt	50
		(Dip 20°–35° N.W.)	

The relationship between these two sections is not known. Since the strike of both groups is similar, there may be a considerable dip fault separating them. Near the road on the W. side of Hope Bowdler [47349246] there are exposures of fine-grained rhyolitic and andesitic tuffs associated with highly weathered doleritic rocks. These are overlain by Harnage Shales.

Hope Bowdler Hill

The Uriconian outcrop of this area is bounded to the N.W. by fault F3 of the Church Stretton Complex and to the N. and S.E. by the Sharpstones and Willstone Hill thrusts respectively. The principal rock types are rhyolites, rhyolitic tuffs, grits and conglomerates with intrusions of altered dolerite. The structure of the area appears to be an anticline with a N.E.–S.W. axis through the summit of Hope Bowdler Hill. The stratigraphical sequence is uncertain but appears to be in downward order as follows:

3. Andesites
2. Conglomerates
1. Rhyolites and andesites with tuff bands.

RHYOLITES AND ANDESITES WITH TUFF BANDS

Except near the Gaer Stone [47209338] there are few exposures of this group which consists of rhyolitic and andesitic lavas and tuffs cut in intricate fashion by numerous ramifying dolerite intrusions. To the N.E. on Willstone Hill, the crags of Battle Stones [48589440] and those to the S.E. are composed of fine-grained pink rhyolitic tuffs with some coarser beds containing fragments of purple rhyolite and pink feldspar crystals. The dip of the tuffs is 30°E. almost exactly opposite to that of the overlying conglomerate and this anomaly may be due to folding or possibly a local unconformity. The proximity of the conglomerate at Battle Stones to acid tuffs and altered dolerites suggests correlation of these tuffs with the similar rhyolitic beds of the Gaer Stone. Elsewhere on Willstone Hill, the conglomerates overlie altered dolerites.

CONGLOMERATES

Conglomerates crop out on the W. side of Hope Bowdler Hill and on Willstone Hill where they form an arcuate outcrop with a dip mainly S.E. but swinging to S.W. at the E. end of the outcrop. The mapping suggests that these occurrences belong to the same horizon and this provides the main indication of a N.E.–S.W. anticline across the summit of Hope Bowdler Hill. The conglomerate matrix is generally dark grey but in fine-grained varieties it is locally light brown. Pebbles include quartz, quartzite, pink feldspar and igneous rocks, mainly of basic composition.

ANDESITES

The conglomerates of Willstone Hill are overlain by amygdaloidal andesite and highly epidotized rocks, possibly andesites or tuffs containing andesite lapilli. The higher beds in this area are cut out by the Willstone Hill Thrust. On the W. side of Hope Bowdler Hill the conglomerates are overlain by green and purple, flow-brecciated andesites and altered dolerites, locally amygdaloidal and commonly epidotic. An isolated exposure of rhyolite which may possibly overlie the andesites occurs at [47479384] close to fault F3.

There are large outcrops of dolerite W. and N. of the Gaer Stone and on Willstone Hill. The interpenetration of dolerite and rhyolite is well exposed N.E. of the Gaer Stone, the dolerite locally forming distinct veins in the rhyolite while in some places xenoliths of rhyolite are only remnants of the country rock.

Cardington Hill

The Uriconian outcrop of the Cardington Hill area extends from Hope Bowdler to the E. limit of the map. It is bounded to the N. by the Willstone Hill and Sharpstones thrusts, is limited to the S. by an unconformable cover of Harnage Shales and possibly has a faulted boundary against the Uriconian of the Hazler Hill area to the W. The stratigraphical sequence is thought to be that shown in the vertical section accompanying the map and it is possible that the rocks form a syncline, the axis of which trends N.W.–S.E. through the head of Hope Batch [477934]. This structure is indicated by the dip of flow banding in the two separate outcrops of the Woodgate Batch Dacites and Andesites, dips in the S.W. outcrop [475930] being to the N.E. while dips in the N.E. outcrop [485935] are to the S.W.

NORTH HILL DACITES

The outcrop of the North Hill Dacites trends S.E. from North Hill [496942] and is partly separated from the Sharpstones Thrust by an outcrop of quartz-porphyry. The rocks are fine grained and pink or purple and grey in colour, leached to pale pink or white where weathered.

MIDDLE HILL ANDESITES AND DACITES

This group is named from its outcrop on Middle Hill [493937], the most striking rock type being a porphyritic lava with white feldspar phenocrysts up to 5 mm long and occasional quartz phenocrysts in a fine green matrix. A finer-grained variety contains pink feldspar phenocrysts and numerous chloritic amygdales, and fine-grained non-porphyritic rocks are also present. South-east of Sandford Seat [46809324] there is a small area which may be occupied by rocks of the Middle Hill group on the W. limb of the syncline. The only two exposures are of vitric tuff and andesite [47109306] 370 yd S.S.W. of the Gaer Stone and a short distance W. of sections of Woodgate Batch rocks.

WOODGATE BATCH DACITES AND ANDESITES

In their two separate outcrops the rocks of this group commonly weather to form crags. They are well exposed in the valley [487935], here called Woodgate Batch, N. of Woodgate Cottage [48689288], where they are brecciated in places and display conspicuous flow banding which dips S.W. at up to 60°. The upper part of a quarry section [48789340] in the valley shows roughly spheroidal andesite, red, green and grey in colour with pink feldspars. The spheroids are about 1 ft across by several feet in length and are surrounded by rotten amygdaloidal material, the amygdales lying parallel to their margins. The lower part of the quarry shows about 18 ft of massive porphyritic andesite, blue, greenish or pale pink in colour with red or pink phenocrysts. The rock is well jointed and is cut by purple and yellow veins of rotten rock up to 1½ in across. In the S.W. outcrop of the group a section in an old quarry [47589262] at Hope Bowdler shows about 25 ft of purple and pink porphyritic dacite, locally sheared. Similar rocks are exposed northwards towards the Gaer Stone. Local flow banding dips 30°–46° N.N.E.

WOODGATE TUFFS

The outcrop of the Woodgate Tuffs extends N.W. from Woodgate Cottage across the middle part of Hope Batch [478932]. The rocks are softer than the adjacent dacites and andesites and exposures are few. They consist of green and pink lithic tuffs with fragments about $\frac{1}{2}$ in across and grits with grains of quartz and pink feldspar.

HOPE BATCH DACITES

At the head of Hope Batch [478934] there are several exposures of green dacite. Their relationship to other rocks of the area is uncertain but it is suggested that they overlie the Woodgate Tuffs in the core of the syncline.

3/PRE-CAMBRIAN: LONGMYNDIAN

The outcrop of the Longmyndian occupies the area W. of the Church Stretton Fault Complex and the outcrop of Carboniferous rocks in the N.E. The vertical section of the map shows a division into the Stretton Series which occupies the E. part of the outcrop, and the Wentnor Series which lies to the W. These names are due to Lapworth (1910) who subdivided the Stretton Series into the Stretton Shale, Burway, Synalds, Lightspout and Portway groups. The subdivisions of the Wentnor Series arise from the work of Whitehead (*in* Pocock and others 1938), who proposed the names Bayston, Bridges and Oakswood groups, and Whittard (1952) and James (1952; 1956) who suggested that the Bayston and Oakswood outcrops were parts of the same group on the E. and W. limbs respectively of a deep syncline.

The Longmyndian sequence consists of shales, siltstones and sandstones, varying from purple to greenish grey in colour with thin bands of tuff at some horizons, some coarse grits and three markedly conglomeratic layers. In general the rocks of the Wentnor Series are coarser and more sandy than those of the Stretton Series but the whole succession is probably of shallow-water deposition, and at some levels, notably in the Burway and Synalds groups there are surface markings on mudstones and siltstones which are probably bubble impressions and possibly rain pits (Dearnley, *in* Greig and others 1968, p. 65), and which would be expected to have formed in silts and muds exposed between tide levels. Some of these marks were formerly thought to be worm burrows and were named by Salter (1856; 1857) as *Arenicolites*. Detailed examination of Salter's type specimens by Dearnley (*in* Greig and others 1968, p. 72) has revealed no evidence of worm burrows so that there is no record as yet of animal life from the Longmyndian.

The Longmyndian rocks are thought to be folded into a deep syncline with both limbs dipping steeply N.W. so that the N.W. limb is slightly overturned (James 1956, fig. 4). The core of the fold lies in the Bridges Group (Section 1) which crops out in the N.W. corner of the map and the axis of the fold trends N.N.E.–S.S.W. parallel with the limbs. James found that in the Linley area, W. of the Long Mynd, rocks of the W. limb of the Bayston–Oakswood Group rested unconformably against Uriconian rocks, but that this sequence was inverted. He concluded that the absence of the Stretton Series on the W. side of the syncline was due to an unconformity at the base of the Bayston–Oakswood Group which would result in the cutting-out of successively younger members of the Stretton Series if the unconformity were traced westwards around the deep downfold.

James (1952 and 1956, p. 322) noted that at some localities, sedimentary structural evidence, such as graded bedding and current bedding, indicated that the rocks were overturned and it was mainly upon this evidence that his suggestion of an overturned synclinal structure was based. Within the area of the geological map the Longmyndian outcrop forms the uninverted E. limb of the fold except for the Bridges Group which lies in the core. Observations of graded and current bedding outside of the Bridges Group generally indicate that younger beds come on to the W. and markings on bedding surfaces, such as bubble impressions, may also be used to deduce the direction of stratigraphical sequence. In the Bridges Group between Bridges and Wentnor, W. of the sheet boundary, sedimentary structures from neighbouring exposures indicate that the rocks young in opposing directions (Wright *in* Greig and others 1968, p. 49) and it is suggested that these apparent reversals of sequence may be due to tightly packed isoclinal folds in the core of the major structure. It is admitted that no hinges of any such folds have been observed in the rather limited exposures available.

Whitehead (*in* Pocock and others 1938, p. 9) noted that the Longmyndian has been regarded as Pre-Cambrian mainly because the great thickness of Longmyndian sediments (possibly about 22,000 ft) cannot be fitted into the known Cambrian or Lower Ordovician sequences of Shropshire. In the Cwms area [474944] the basal Cambrian quartzite rests unconformably upon a faulted outcrop of weathered reddish grits, tentatively correlated with some part of the Wentnor Series, but apart from this locality, the oldest rocks known to rest directly upon Longmyndian are shales of Upper Ordovician age in the Pontesbury area, 8 miles N.W. of Church Stretton. Lapworth (1910, p. 747) stated that the Western Longmyndian (Wentnor Series) . . . "is probably closely related to the Torridonian rocks of Scotland". This correlation has received support from the work of Creer (1957, p. 214) on the natural remanent magnetization of rocks from the Wentnor Series. He found a close comparison between the axes of magnetization of Upper Torridonian and Wentnor rocks and suggested that the two groups are of approximately equal, Pre-Cambrian, age.

Stretton Series

STRETTON SHALE GROUP

The Stretton Shale Group is known in two outcrops on either side of fault F1 of the Church Stretton Complex. The western outcrop extends from Minton [431907] to Brownhill [473972] being limited to the W. by the outcrop of the Buxton Rock and to the E. by faults and an unconformable cover of *Pentamerus* Beds. The eastern outcrop lies between Little Stretton [444916] and Caradoc Coppice [468948] being bounded to E. and W. by F1 and the outcrop of the Ragleth Tuffs respectively. The two outcrops were distinguished by Lapworth as the Brockhurst and Watling shales but in this account they are considered as one group, although the stratigraphical relationship between them cannot be determined because of the fault separating them. Exposures in the shales are relatively scarce in the drift-covered lower parts of the Church Stretton valley but there are more outcrops on the steep slopes on the W. side of the valley, particularly near the mouths of the batches entering the main valley, and the Helmeth Grit is fairly well exposed on the eastern slopes.

The Helmeth Grit rests upon Uriconian rocks on Ragleth, Hazler and Helmeth hills and the outcrop terminates at its N. and S. ends against fault F1. The map shows the Grit overlying both Ragleth Tuffs and Cwms Rhyolites in the vicinity of Caradoc Coppice and this evidence, together with the marked divergence in strike between the Uriconian of the Caer Caradoc area and the Longmyndian, suggests that there may be an unconformity at the base of the Helmeth Grit. This was not the conclusion of Cobbold and Whittard (1935) who described the Grit as four massive gritty bands within a 100-ft sequence of green and purple shales, and noted (1935, p. 354) that the so-called grits are better described as lithic tuffs, formed largely of fragments derived from the Uriconian by volcanic processes. Thus the Helmeth Grit may represent the dying phase of Uriconian vulcanicity and form a passage from the Uriconian to the Longmyndian.

The Helmeth Grit crops out at the S.W. end of Ragleth Wood [44739180], in Ragleth Wood [44949225] S.S.E. of Brockhurst Castle, and along the Hazler Old Road [465933]. Cobbold and Whittard's (1935) map does not show the Grit north of Helmeth Hill [469938] but the Geological Survey continued the mapped outcrop to Caradoc Coppice mainly from the evidence of grit debris and some small exposures. This mapping is supported by the record of a magnetic anomaly in the area (Brooks *in* Greig and others 1968, p. 316) which may be due to the Helmeth Grit.

There are scattered exposures of the Stretton Shales along the N.W. flanks of Ragleth Hill and greenish grey shales also crop out in a sunken lane [46479400] S.W. of New House Farm. At Minton [430908] the group is cut out by overstep of Upper Llandovery rocks but the outcrop widens to the N. and grey shales, commonly weathered, are exposed in the lower parts of Callow Hollow [432912], Ashes Hollow [440923] and the Cardingmill Valley [451941] and E. of Castle Hill [462960], All Stretton. Carbonate nodules in the shales have been noted in exposures at Church Stretton and All Stretton (James *in* Whittard and others 1953, p. 238). The shales generally dip steeply W.N.W. and the cleavage, where distinct from the bedding, may dip steeply W.N.W. or E.S.E. Minor variations of dip occur at some localities as in the Burway Road section [45149398] where there is a small anticline with the hinge striking N.N.E.–S.S.W. In a section [46229588] 50 yd N. of St. Michael's Church, All Stretton, the bedding dips at 55° E.S.E. and the cleavage dips steeply N.W. giving rise to a cleavage-bedding lineation which plunges N.E. at 20°. At the All Stretton war memorial, 300 yd to the S. the apparent steep dip to W.N.W. is due to closely spaced cleavage planes.

BURWAY GROUP

The outcrop of the Burway Group lies immediately W. of the Stretton Shale Group and extends from Priors Holt Hill [419901] in the S. to near Leebotwood in the N. There are no exposures of Burway rocks N. of Lower Wood [463976] and the mapping of the Group in the drift-covered ground to the N. is entirely conjectural.

The lower and upper limits of the Group are marked by the Buxton Rock and the Cardingmill Grit respectively. At its type locality in Buxton Quarry, All Stretton [459955], the Buxton Rock forms a 24-ft vertical bed of massive, fine-grained, greenish grey cherty rock with small black spots locally and with thin quartz veins on joints. It is a siliceous dust tuff and consists mostly of finely divided clay minerals, chlorite, quartz and feldspar. The band can be traced at intervals where it crosses the main valleys from near Dudgeley [46639666] in the N. to near Minton [430908] in the S. where it is unconformably overstepped by Upper Llandovery rocks.

The main part of the Burway Group comprises flaggy greenish grey mudstones, siltstones and sandstones with more massive sandstone bands at some horizons. The siltstones and mudstones are laminated locally and there are occasional bands of siltstone or mudstone which are purple or purplish grey in colour. In common with the rest of the Stretton Series the Burway Group is best exposed on the sides of the major valleys and there are only small scattered outcrops on the intervening spurs. The most continuous section is in Ashes Hollow [436929] where there are extensive exposures of vertical, uniformly flaggy siltstones and sandstones. The regional dip is steep to W.N.W. but in some areas, as near Lower Wood [46669735], Inwood [46269678] and Burway Hill [44809413] the dip is south-easterly with values ranging from about 40° to 75°. These S.E. dips are present in a zone which lies 250–450 yd N.W. of the Buxton Rock, suggesting the existence of minor anticlinal structures (see Section 1 below map), possibly arranged *en echelon* along the outcrop of the Group.

The Cardingmill Grit of this account is the equivalent of the Lower Cardingmill Grit of James (1956, p. 317) who described a lower and an upper grit, the latter being purplish in colour and placed by him in the lower part of the succeeding Synalds Group. The Geological Survey found that while purple sandstone bands occurred in the basal beds of the Synalds Group at some localities, for example Batch valley [44949568], they were not sufficiently persistent or distinctive to be separated as the Upper Cardingmill Grit.

The Cardingmill Grit is a massive, micaceous, greenish grey sandstone, about 80–100 ft thick and with occasional thin siltstone partings. Current bedding indicating a westward stratigraphical sequence has been recorded from the Batch valley. At its type locality in the Cardingmill Valley [44369460] and on the sides of the other major valleys to the N.E. and S.W., the Grit forms fairly prominent crags, the shape of which is controlled by strong vertical and horizontal joints. In these sections the line of the outcrop is commonly disrupted by minor faults which give rise to small dextral and sinistral displacements. On the intervening ridges the Grit forms a series of minor summits such as Grindle Hill [430926] and Bodbury Hill [445948] but on the higher ground it is poorly exposed and the line of the outcrop is generalized on the map. It is probably as much disrupted by minor faults as are the better exposed valley sections.

SYNALDS GROUP

The outcrop of the Synalds Group lies W. of the Cardingmill Grit and extends over the length of the Long Mynd almost to the Betchcott Brook W. of Leebotwood. The mapping of the N. end of the outcrop is conjectural, the most northerly exposures of the Group occurring S.W. of Hodghurst [457978]. The base of the Group is defined by the top of the Cardingmill Grit and the upper limit is taken at the change in colour from the dominantly purple Synalds rocks to the greenish grey rocks of the Lightspout Group to the W. In well-exposed areas this change is visible in a small thickness of rocks and is quite well marked. The group contains several tuffaceous horizons among which are the Batch Volcanic beds, first named by Cobbold (1900, p. 72).

The Synalds Group consists mainly of purple shaly mudstones and siltstones, locally laminated, with subordinate bands of greenish grey sandstone up to several feet thick. The regional bedding dip is steep to W.N.W. but the shaly rocks commonly exhibit a strong cleavage which is vertical or dips steeply E.S.E. Cleavage and bedding may have the same strike but at some localities there may be a divergence in strike of about 20° between the two. The Cardingmill Valley below the Pike [442949] and the Batch valley [449961] S.W. of Jinlye are good localities for the study of these structural features. At some horizons there are thin beds of greenish grey sediment but in Callow Hollow and Ashes Hollow there is a considerable thickness of green siltstone and sandstone in the lower part of the Group. In Ashes Hollow [432931] about 400 ft of greenish grey beds are separated from the Cardingmill Grit by about 200 ft of purple beds, the width of outcrop of the green rocks being increased considerably near the valley bottom by a major sigmoid flexure in strike, which is apparently confined to the Synalds Group. At some localities, as in the Cardingmill and Batch valleys, the mudstones are notable for the abundance of bedding-plane markings which have been referred to as rain pits, bubble impressions and worm burrows. As indicated on p. 15 further examination of the alleged worm burrows has shown no evidence that they are of organic origin.

North of Ashes Hollow the two most persistent bands of tuff in the Synalds Group have been grouped together as the Batch Volcanic beds and have been called the Andesitic Ash (lower band) and White Ash (upper band) respectively (Cobbold 1900, p. 77). They are fairly distinctive lithologically, the lowest part of the Andesitic Ash being pale green with dark patches and the upper part purple with conspicuous dark green patches. The White Ash is almost white or very pale green and carries small dark green patches.

These bands can be traced at intervals from Ashes Hollow N.E. to the vicinity of Womerton [456972] and maintain constant positions relative to the top of the Synalds Group. In the northern part of the Long Mynd a third tuff band occurs between the Andesitic and White ashes and a fourth band lies above the White Ash. In the type area of the Batch valley, All Stretton, all four tuffs are exposed on the spur which rises westwards from the junction [44709605] of Jonathan's Hollow and Long Batch. The section on this spur reading downwards from W. to E. is as follows:

	Thickness in ft
Base of Lightspout Group	
Purple shales with sandstone bands	70
Tuff, greenish grey, fine-grained	7
Purple shales with sandstone bands	120
White Ash, moderately coarse pale greenish tuff	7
Purple shales	40
Tuff, pale greenish, fine-grained with some coarser bands	15
Purple shales with sandstone bands	150
Andesitic Ash, moderately coarse tuff, pale green in lower part, purple in upper part	16

The two unnamed tuffs in this section have not been traced as continuously as the two named bands and this is also true of a 10-ft tuff found only in the Devilsmouth area [439944] about 500 ft above the base of the Synalds Group.

South of Ashes Hollow the tuffs are all rather similar in appearance being moderately coarse and varying from greenish to purplish grey in colour. It is therefore difficult to identify the Andesitic and White ashes in this area and the tuffs appear to be less persistent laterally and to occupy less constant horizons within the group.

Petrographic examination shows that the tuffs are all of a similar character with a finely divided matrix composed mainly of clay minerals, micaceous aggregate, epidote and chlorite, enclosing fragments of feldspar, quartz, biotite, mudstone, siltstone, fine-grained igneous rocks and irregular aggregates of chlorite, micaceous material and epidote. The last-named inclusions may be fragments of older pyro-clastic rocks, possibly of Uriconian age, and the igneous rock fragments are mainly rhyolitic or andesitic in composition. The occurrence of tuffs in the Longmyndian indicates that the volcanic activity of Uriconian times was not entirely extinct. Although the tuffs crop out over a wide area in the Long Mynd they are of relatively uniform thickness and provide no indication of the situation of the volcanic source of the material, although of course it may well have lain in the vicinity of the present Uriconian outcrops.

LIGHTSPOUT GROUP

The outcrop of the Lightspout Group extends from the S.W. corner of the map to the N. boundary of the area N.N.W. of Leebotwood and is considerably displaced laterally along the N.–S. Yewtree Bank and Ashes Hollow faults in the southern part of the Long Mynd. The most northerly exposures of Lightspout rocks are at Deadman's Batch [44849782] and the mapping in the drift-covered ground E. of Woolstaston is conjectural. The base of the group is taken at the change from dominantly purple Synalds rocks to the generally greenish grey Lightspout sediments. In many sections this change is accompanied by a westward transition from shales with subordinate sandstones (Synalds) to more flaggy mudstones and siltstones with massive and more abundant sandstones (Lightspout), but in the N. part of the Long Mynd the lowest 150 ft of the group consist mainly of flaggy siltstone with very little sandstone. The top of the group is defined by the base of the Huckster Conglomerate which overlies about 400 ft of purple shaly mudstones and siltstones with bands of coarse purplish grey sandstone. These topmost beds of the Lightspout Group are comparable with the rocks of the Synalds Group and contain at least two impersistent bands of tuff, similar to the Batch Volcanic beds.

Between about 150 ft and 500 ft above the base there are several bands of pale-weathering, massive sandstone, well exposed in the Cardingmill Valley on the S. side of Haddon Hill [438951] and at Jonathan's Rock [446965]. One of these bands was separated by James (1956, p. 318) as the Haddon Hill Grit but the Geological Survey considered that no single band of sandstone was sufficiently distinctive or persistent to be classed as a separate grit horizon. The regional dip of the Lightspout rocks is steep to W.N.W. and the cleavage in the shaly beds is generally vertical or steep with a strike only slightly divergent from that of the bedding. In the type area of Lightspout Hollow [430950] the rocks exposed are characteristic of the greater part of the group, consisting of greenish grey sandstones, rather massive and well jointed with thinner bands of finer flaggy sandstone, siltstone and mudstone. The competent sandstones are cut along tension cracks and joints by thin quartz veins which are not seen in the siltstones and shales. There are occasional bands of purple sandstone and siltstone but these are generally subordinate in amount.

The bands of tuff at the top of the Lightspout Group are important in a discussion of the unconformity which James (1956, p. 319) considered to occur at the base of the Huckster Conglomerate. On this and other evidence he renamed the Portway Group as the 'Mintonian' and raised it to a status comparable with the Stretton and Wentnor series. At Deadman's Batch [44909783] he discovered a tuff band in purple shales and sandstones lying about 250 ft below the Huckster Conglomerate and identified it with the Batch Volcanic beds (1956, p. 329), concluding that the associated purple sediments belonged to the Synalds Group. James thus deduced that the Huckster Conglomerate at Deadman's Batch rested directly upon the Synalds Group and suggested an unconformity to account for the absence of the Lightspout Group. Subsequent to James's work the Geological Survey (Greig and Wright 1959) found bands of tuff in purple beds at the top of the Lightspout Group in the Mott Road valley [432955], Ashes Hollow [42249378] and near Narnell's Rock [42209332], and in ground S. of the area of the map near Black Knoll [392886] and Plowden [386878]. These occurrences cast considerable doubt on James's identification of the purple rocks at Deadman's Batch with the Synalds Group, so that in this account Lapworth's name Portway Group is retained for the rocks above the Huckster Conglomerate and no unconformity has been mapped at its base.

Portway Group

The outcrop of the Portway Group extends across the Long Mynd, mainly on the poorly exposed summit plateau, from the S.W. corner of the map to the N. limit of the area W. of Leebotwood. Apart from small scattered stream sections in the Woolstaston [452984] area, the most northerly exposures occur in Hawkham [433975] and High Park [440975] hollows and the mapped boundaries N. of this area are largely conjectural. The lower limit of the group is taken at the base of the Huckster Conglomerate which is well developed and moderately well exposed S. of the Asterton area [400910] locally reaching a thickness of 60 ft. Within the area of the map, however, the conglomerate is poorly developed and in places is no more than a pebbly sandstone. It is exposed only in the main valley sections and the outcrop as shown on the map is therefore generalized and is probably much more disrupted by minor faults than has been indicated. The top of the group is taken at the change from purple and green shaly siltstones and sandstones (Portway Group) to the more massive, coarse purple and grey sandstones of the Bayston–Oakswood Group. In the area of the map, the junction is exposed only at the N. end of the Long Mynd in Hawkham Hollow. There are no sections near the top of the Portway Group S. of this locality and the base of the Bayston–Oakswood Group has in general been mapped conjecturally at a constant distance below the Darnford Conglomerate.

The Portway rocks largely consist of purple and green shaly mudstones and siltstones with purple and green sandstone bands abundant locally. In the upper parts of Callow Hollow [413928] and Ashes Hollow [423941] and at Deadman's Batch [447978] there are sections in the lower part of the group showing about 100 ft of massive purplish sandstone immediately W. of the Huckster Conglomerate, succeeded westwards by banded siltstones and sandstones. Siltstones and sandstones in the higher part of the group are exposed in strike sections in Hawkham and High Park hollows.

Evidence of unconformity between the Stretton and Wentnor series

Within the area of the map there are no sections showing an unconformable relationship between the Stretton and Wentnor series. Evidence on this point comes mainly from other areas in the Welsh Borders and has been reviewed by Whittard (1952, p. 146). The coarser sandy rocks characteristic of the Wentnor Series are of greater geographical extent than those of the Stretton Series, the latter being confined to the Long Mynd–Shrewsbury outcrop and to a few small fault-bounded blocks occurring close by, on the line of the Church Stretton Fault Complex. Rocks of Wentnor Series type occur in the Long Mynd–Shrewsbury outcrop and outside it, in the inliers of Pedwardine, Old Radnor and Huntley in Gloucestershire. Whittard suggested that this implied a widespread and violent overstep of the Wentnor Series. There is a marked decrease in the width of the outcrop of the Portway Group southward across the Long Mynd and although the mapping of the top of the Group is only conjectural, the marker horizons of the Huckster (Portway Group) and Darnford (Bayston–Oakswood Group) conglomerates converge southwards in a manner suggesting a southward narrowing of the Portway outcrop, possibly by an unconformity at the base of the Bayston–Oakswood Group. On Haughmond Hill near Shrewsbury, the basal member of the Wentnor Series, the Haughmond Conglomerate, rests upon beds possibly equivalent to the lower part of the Synalds Group, which would imply that between the Long Mynd and Shrewsbury the Portway, Lightspout and (upper) Synalds groups are cut out by an unconformity. James's (1956) interpretation of a major synclinal structure for the Longmyndian with the Stretton Series occurring only on the E. limb of the fold involves the suggestion of an unconformity at the base of the Wentnor Series, cutting out the Stretton Series westwards around the fold.

Wentnor Series

BAYSTON–OAKSWOOD GROUP

The outcrop of the Bayston–Oakswood Group covers the W. part of the Long Mynd from the S.W. margins of the area to the N. limit of the map, N.E. and N.W. of Picklescott [437995], the rocks forming part of the E. limb of the Longmyndian syncline. The base of the Group is exposed only in Hawkham Hollow [432976] and is taken at the change from purple and green shales and sandstones of the Portway Group to the more massive, coarse purplish sandstone above. There is no obvious angular discordance at this horizon but the lithological change is well marked, and the basal sandstone of the Group contains small scattered pebbles which James (1956, p. 319) suggested might represent the dying out of the Haughmond Conglomerate which marks the base of the Group in the Shrewsbury area. The top of the Group is taken at the change from massive sandstones to the more flaggy laminated siltstones and sandstones of the Bridges Group. The rocks are poorly exposed along this boundary and its transitional character was noted by James (1956, p. 322) who commented that the delineation of the boundary was arbitrary.

The Bayston–Oakswood rocks are mainly coarse, massive purplish sandstones, locally gritty and with occasional sandstone bands. There are two marker horizons, the Darnford and Stanbatch conglomerates, the former taking its name from exposures in Colliersford Gutter [426973], 250 yd S. of Upper Darnford. Here there are about 30 ft of coarse conglomerate with rounded pebbles, up to about 2 in across, of quartz, quartzite, rhyolite and scarce pink granite. The conglomerate is overlain by flaggy green siltstones which are also found in other sections to the S. Between Darnford and Stanbatch [407935] the conglomerate is traced only from small scattered exposures and soil debris, but S. of Stanbatch there are extensive exposures on the western scarp slope of the Long Mynd and the outcrop is disrupted by a number of minor transcurrent faults. The type locality of the Stanbatch Conglomerate is at Stanbatch [406936] whence it can be traced N.N.E. to the northern limit of the map. There are no exposures S. of Stanbatch in the low ground W. of the Long Mynd. It is better exposed than the Darnford Conglomerate and most of the major valley sections display a double-ribbed topographic feature made by two bands of conglomerate separated by a band of softer sandstone. The most extensive section is probably that on the Ratlinghope road [415956] where there are 200 ft of conglomerate, separated from an upper 60-ft conglomerate to the W. by 70 ft of soft coarse purple sandstone. The pebbles are well rounded, up to about 2 in across and consist mainly of quartz or quartzite with lesser amounts of rhyolite and felsite. In the lower band the reddish brown silty matrix is very strong where it is not weathered, and pebbles can be broken across with the hammer, rather than separated from the matrix. In this section there is some suggestion of a westward decrease in pebble size in accordance with the accepted view of an E.–W. stratigraphical sequence, but this gradation is not well marked. The map shows the outcrops of the Stanbatch and Darnford conglomerates disrupted by a number of transcurrent faults trending about E.–W. or E.S.E.–W.N.W. These have been mapped mainly in the exposed valley sections and the generalized outcrops on the intervening spurs may be more broken up by faults than has been shown.

Dearnley (*in* Greig and others 1968, p. 57) made a petrological study of pebbles from the conglomerates throughout the Longmyndian outcrop and found that they included low-grade metamorphic quartzite, quartz-schist and quartz-muscovite-schist, rhyolites including flow-banded, spherulitic and devitrified types, rare andesite, basalt and more abundant granophyre and quartz-porphyry, tuffs of various types including welded tuffs or ignimbrites, and rare pebbles of quartzitic sandstone and subgreywacke. The igneous rock types above are all known from the Uriconian and their presence in the conglomerates substantiates opinions of earlier workers that the Longmyndian was derived in considerable part by erosion of Uriconian outcrops.

BRIDGES GROUP

The outcrop of the Bridges Group occurs in the N.W. corner of the map and there is a very narrow strip on the W. margin of the area at Medlicott [400946]. The rocks comprise purple siltstones and sandstones, commonly laminated and moderately flaggy, the well-marked bedding and the higher proportion of silty sediment serving to distinguish them from the coarser, more massive beds of the Bayston–Oakswood Group. The junction between the two groups is not well marked in the area of the map and the mapped boundary is somewhat arbitrary.

The Group is thought to occupy the core of the Longmyndian syncline and in exposures between Bridges and Wentnor, W. of the Long Mynd, evidence from sedimentary structures suggests that there are repeated reversals of age sequence, possibly due to closely packed minor isoclinal folds. There are few exposures showing these features within the area of the map, but at [40669766], 200 yd S.E. of Castle Ring, poor graded bedding in steeply dipping purple siltstones and sandstones indicates that the succession is to the W. Exposures of similar rocks occur on the ridge S.W. of Castle Ring, on the valley side between Stitt [403985] and New Leasowes [405997], in the valley between Thresholds [411994] and Lower Darnford [416978], and in Rookery Wood [402970], 300 yd N.W. of Ratlinghope.

FAULTED INLIERS OF THE WENTNOR SERIES

Cwms Area

In the Cwms area [474940] there is a triangular outcrop of grits and conglomerates, bounded to E. and W. by F2 and F3 of the Church Stretton Fault Complex and overlain to the N.E. by the basal Cambrian quartzite. They are rather poorly exposed and are much weathered locally, but Cobbold (1927, p. 551) suggested that they might be part of the Wentnor Series. If this correlation is correct then this outcrop provides the only direct evidence of a Pre-Cambrian age for the Longmyndian.

Little Stretton Area

At the S. end of Ragleth Hill [446915] there is an outcrop, measuring about 300 yd by 50 yd, of red and pink conglomerate and grit, assigned by Cobbold and Whittard (1935,

p. 349) to the Wentnor Series. There is some doubt as to the nature of the junction of these beds with the Uriconian to the N. but to the S. they are overlain unconformably by Harnage Shales.

Dolerite Intrusions in the Longmyndian

The dolerites of the Long Mynd occur mainly as dykes cutting the steeply folded sediments but there are a small number of intrusive bosses and some steeply inclined concordant sheets which could be regarded as sills folded with the sediments, but more probably belong to a post-folding phase of dyke intrusion. The dykes vary in thickness from a few feet to 200 ft but are more commonly up to about 10 ft across. Trends are difficult to establish because of the generally restricted nature of the outcrops but in some instances dykes have been traced for about ½ mile. There appears to be a dominant trend approximately E.–W. and another less well defined direction about N.W.–S.E. Exposures of dolerite can be seen on Packetstone Hill [41909132], in Sleekstonebank Hollow [42489178], in Ashes Hollow near Little Stretton [44139220] and near Narnell's Rock [42229377], near Worldsend, Church Stretton [450936], in Bilbatch [409957] and near The Villa [437975].

In hand specimen the fresher dolerites are massive, eucrystalline bluish grey rocks with clear feldspar and small amounts of visible pyrite. In the more altered varieties or on weathered surfaces the ferromagnesian minerals are dark green and the feldspar is opaque and white or pinkish in colour. The rocks all appear to belong to the quartz-dolerite suite and under the microscope they show good ophitic texture with subhedral plagioclase prisms, partly or wholly enclosed by anhedral augite. Anhedral interstitial quartz occurs in some specimens but in others the acid magmatic residuum may be represented solely by chloritized patches of mesostasis. Chlorite, generally penninitic, is also common as partial or complete replacement of augite. Accessory minerals include ilmenite or titanomagnetite, apatite and pyrite.

In the Long Mynd and Shelve areas of Shropshire, intrusive dolerites cut Uriconian, Longmyndian, Cambrian and

Ordovician rocks but intrusions in the Ordovician occur only W. of the Church Stretton Fault Complex. The basaltic lavas and doleritic intrusions of the Uriconian of the Church Stretton area are generally extensively altered but they are similar to some of the more altered intrusions of the Long Mynd. The Uriconian lavas are clearly Pre-Cambrian and the dolerite intrusions in the Uriconian are probably Pre-Cambrian and possibly pre-Longmyndian in age. The evidence for this is that the main dolerite intrusion of The Lawley terminates abruptly against the Cambrian quartzite which does not seem to be affected by it (Robertson *in* Pocock and others 1938, p. 32), while the dolerites of Caer Caradoc Hill are involved in folds and thrusts which appear to be older than the Longmyndian. Blyth (1944, p. 169) considered that the basic intrusions of the Shelve area were emplaced during or after the folding of the Ordovician (Arenig to Caradoc) sediments but prior to the deposition of the basal Silurian (Upper Llandovery) rocks of the area. Many of the Long Mynd dolerites are similar to rocks from the Shelve described by Blyth.

The Long Mynd intrusions thus show similarities to the Ordovician and Uriconian dolerites but since they are younger than the intense folding which affected the Longmyndian they are most probably younger than the intrusions in the Uriconian. In the absence of more conclusive evidence it is suggested that the Long Mynd dolerites are approximately contemporaneous with those of the Shelve and were intruded in post-Caradoc times but before the deposition of the Upper Llandovery rocks. The apparent absence of dykes in the Caradoc Series E. of the Church Stretton Fault Complex suggests that this structure may have acted as a barrier to the doleritic magma.

4/CAMBRIAN

Cambrian rocks crop out in the Comley area [485965] on the E. side of Caer Caradoc and The Lawley and are involved in the Church Stretton Fault Complex. The Cambrian rests unconformably on Uriconian and on possible Longmyndian rocks in the Cwms area [475944] and is overlain with unconformity by the Hoar Edge Grit of Ordovician (Caradoc Series) age. The succession of Cambrian rocks is shown in the vertical section accompanying the geological map.

The Comley area is well known to geologists for the classic stratigraphical research of the latter part of the 19th century and the earlier part of the present century. A description of the history of Cambrian research in Shropshire was given by Robertson (*in* Pocock and others 1938, p. 59) and the following account is largely abstracted from it. The Wrekin Quartzite was regarded by Murchison (1839) as altered Caradoc Sandstone (Silurian of Murchison's classification) and the Comley Sandstone as volcanic grits. Callaway (1874, p. 196) suggested that the Shineton Shales, which had previously been confused with the Ordovician Harnage Shales, belonged to the Lower Tremadoc Series and later (1877) completely separated the Shineton Shales from the Harnage Shales. In this second account he also recognized the Cambrian age of the Comley Sandstone, which he compared with the Hollybush Sandstone of the Malvern area and called it by that name. Lapworth (1888) recognized from Comley the first Lower Cambrian trilobite to be found in Britain and also the presence of Middle Cambrian fossils there (1891). In 1906 Cobbold began a series of excavations in the Comley area the results of which were published as reports to the British Association for the Advancement of Science between 1909 and 1933 and in the Quarterly Journal of the Geological Society of London between 1910 and 1936. Most of the excavations are now overgrown but it is from this work that we derive most of our knowledge of the Cambrian rocks of the Comley area. Cobbold showed (1927, p. 560) that the thin limestone beds, of about 6 ft total thickness, at the top of the Lower Comley Series could be divided into 5 bands, each except the topmost with a characteristic trilobite fauna. He also demonstrated (1927, p. 568) that the Lower Comley Series was overlain with considerable unconformity by Middle Cambrian rocks, some of which were conglomeratic and contained blocks of fossiliferous Lower Cambrian sandstones, showing that the latter had been folded and eroded prior to the deposition of the Middle Cambrian. In the Upper Cambrian of the Comley area Cobbold (1927) recognized the Grey (*Orusia*) Shales as distinct from the overlying Shineton Shales. Stubblefield and Bulman (1927) confirmed Callaway's opinion that the Shineton Shales were of Tremadoc age, and Stubblefield (1930b) showed that from a comparison with the Cambrian outcrops of other areas, the faunas of the Shropshire rocks indicated slight breaks in the succession between the Middle Cambrian and the *Orusia* Shales, between the latter and the Black Shales which he had discovered in the Shrewsbury District, and between the Black Shales and the Shineton Shales. These breaks however are not marked by contemporaneous folding and unconformity.

Lower Cambrian

WREKIN QUARTZITE

The Wrekin Quartzite covers most of the E. slopes of The Lawley and the mapping suggests that it rests unconformably on the Uriconian to the W. although the junction is not exposed. On Little Caradoc [481960] the quartzite is faulted against Uriconian and dips W. towards the fault. To the S. on the N.E. shoulder of Caer Caradoc [479957] it appears to rest unconformably on the Uriconian and dips E. at about 45°. In this area the rock is a sugary white or blue quartzite, pebbly near the base with fragments of quartz and pink rhyolite. North-west of Hill House [48459575] there is an area in which the occurrence of scattered quartzite blocks

33

suggests the existence of an outcrop of the quartzite. Cobbold (1927) interpreted this as the core of a N.–S. anticline flanked to E. and W. by outcrops of the Lower Comley Series.

In the Cwms [475945] exposures are generally poor but the quartzite appears to rest upon red grits, possibly belonging to the Wentnor Series. An excavation by Cobbold at [47519424] found the lower part of the Lower Comley Series resting on 25 ft of Wrekin Quartzite which was apparently faulted against red sandstone. In an old quarry [47549474], 550 yd to the N., 12 ft of quartzite with black and white patches, pass up into 14 ft of fine-grained fossiliferous glauconitic sandstone forming the base of the Lower Comley Series (Cobbold 1921).

LOWER COMLEY SERIES

Lower Comley Sandstone

In general the Lower Comley Sandstone is poorly exposed and there are no outcrops on the S.E. side of The Lawley. The best known section is at Comley Quarry [48459647] where green glauconitic sandstone dipping E. at 73° forms the W. face. There are more exposures of sandstone on the slope to the S. and a few outcrops occur in and near the stream 450 yd S.S.E. of the quarry.

An inclined borehole put down by the Geological Survey at Shootrough [48899645] penetrated about 420 ft into the Lower Comley Sandstone beneath an unconformable cover of Middle and Upper Cambrian rocks. The sandstone was greenish grey with local purplish coloration, medium-grained and glauconitic in the upper part but fine-grained and silty towards the bottom of the hole.

Lower Comley Limestones

The type section of the Lower Comley Limestones is at Comley Quarry [48459647] where the following divisions are present:

	ft	in
Lapworthella Limestone		
Very dark grey, composed of phosphatic material and occasional quartz pebbles. Locally thinning out . . . . up to		6
Protolenus Limestone		
Pale grey fossiliferous limestone, dark and phosphatic where fossils are rarer . . . . about		6
Strenuella Limestone		
Red to purple sandy limestone with well rounded grains of quartz and a phosphatic matrix . . about		9
Eodiscus bellimarginatus Limestone		
Phosphatic limestone . . . . . about	1	9
Red *Callavia* Sandstone		
Nodules of red or purplish micaceous and glauconitic calcareous sandstone . . . . about	2	6
Green *Callavia* Sandstone		
Bright green glauconitic sandstone . .		

Cobbold found the limestones in a trench [48499625] 200 yd S. of the quarry and in another excavation in the Cwms [47619461]. He described the faunas of the limestones in his papers of 1910, 1921, 1931 and 1936.

Middle Cambrian

UPPER COMLEY SERIES

The Upper Comley Series consists of a sequence of conglomerates, breccias, sandstones and shales which were subdivided by Cobbold as follows (downward stratigraphical order):

	ft
Billingsella Beds, sandy shales with some calcareous beds .	6
Paradoxides davidis Grits, gritty flags with calcareous bands	10
'*P. rugulosus*' Sandstone, soft sandstones with calcareous bands . . . . over 10	
Shales with grit bands . . . . . . ?200–300	
Comley Breccia Bed (*P. intermedius* Grit and Breccia) .	35
'*Dorypyge*' Flags, dark phosphatic sandy flags . . c.5	
Shales with grit bands c.300	
P. groomi Grit and Conglomerate (Quarry Ridge Grit) .	c.30

The *P. groomi* Grit is exposed on the E. side of Comley Quarry, the lowest bed overlying the Lower Comley Limestones being a dark phosphatic layer with *Paradoxides spp.* and *Kootenia* [*Dorypyge*] *lakei* (Cobbold). The Grit is exposed on the ridge to the S., and in an excavation [48499625] 200 yd S. of the quarry Cobbold found a conglomerate up to 12 ft thick, composed of subangular blocks of fossiliferous Lower Cambrian sandstones and limestones in a glauconitic sandy matrix which contained the Middle Cambrian *P. groomi* fauna. The Grit is poorly exposed at Robin's Tump [48349548] where an excavation by Cobbold showed that it rested on the Lower Comley Sandstone with the Lower Comley Limestones cut out by unconformity. However, in the Cwms [47619461] Cobbold's excavation showed that the limestones were present below the basal Middle Cambrian grit which can now only be traced by its topographical feature.

The shales and flags between the *P. groomi* Grit and the Comley Breccia Bed are very poorly exposed, but the Breccia Bed was excavated [48539607] by Cobbold, 370 yd N. of Hill House, and traced by him for 300 yd S. of the excavation. From the S. end of this outcrop Stubblefield (*in* Whittard and others 1953, p. 237) described a section [48469582] which showed a breccia of blocks of fossiliferous Lower Comley Limestones in a glauconitic gritty matrix with Middle Cambrian fossils such as *Helcionella oblonga* Cobbold, *Bailiella cobboldi* Resser and fragments of *Paradoxides*, and with occasional Lower Cambrian forms, possibly remanié fossils separated from their original matrix. On Dairy Hill [48659625], the Breccia Bed rests unconformably on Lower Cambrian sandstones and limestones, and in the road N. of the hill [48639632] there is an exposure of *Callavia* Sandstone (Lower Cambrian) surrounded by Middle Cambrian rocks.

The upper part of the Middle Cambrian is exposed only in a small anticline [48769652] on the road between Comley and Shootrough. In excavations in this area Cobbold found up to 10 ft of the '*P. rugulosus*' Sandstone overlain by 10 ft of the *P. davidis* Grits. About 6 ft of the *Billingsella* Beds are exposed in the Shootrough area and they were also found by Cobbold in an excavation [48609587] 200 yd N.E. of

Hill House, below Upper Cambrian shales.

The Geological Survey inclined borehole [48899645] at Shootrough proved 118 ft (estimated true thickness about 104 ft) of Middle Cambrian rocks below the *Orusia* Shales, the sequence being as follows:

	Thickness in borehole ft
Billingsella Beds	
Sheared calcareous grey sandstones with some glauconite	4
Fault (sheared sandstone)	5
Sandstones and shales	97
?Comley Breccia Bed	
Coarse-grained grey sandstone with angular fragments of dark greenish grey sandstone and pale grey limestone	12

The Breccia Bed rests unconformably on the Lower Comley Sandstone with the lower part of the Middle Cambrian and the Lower Comley Limestones cut out by the unconformity. In the borehole the Breccia Bed contained rock fragments with Lower Cambrian fossils but the matrix yielded no exclusively Middle Cambrian types and appeared to contain Lower Cambrian forms such as *Rhombocorniculum* [*Helenia*] *cancellatum* (Cobbold). It is possible however that these specimens from the matrix were also derived by erosion of Lower Cambrian rocks.

Upper Cambrian

Upper Cambrian shales crop out in the gap between Comley and The Lawley, in the low ground E. of The Lawley and S.W. of Shootrough, W. of the Wilderness ridge. In general the rocks are soft and easily weathered so that they form low ground in which they are seldom exposed. The Upper Cambrian rocks of Shropshire have been divided into the following (downward) sequence:

Shineton Shales   (Tremadoc)

Black Shales

Grey (*Orusia*) Shales   } (Dolgelly)

Because of the general lack of exposures in the Comley area, it is not possible to map out these subdivisions and they are shown on the geological map as one group.

Grey micaceous shales and siltstones containing fossils indicative of the *Orusia* Shales are exposed in the stream [48589667] 250–350 yd N.N.E. of Comley Quarry and in a stream [48729651] 300 yd at 075° from Comley Quarry. The Shootrough Borehole proved 95 ft (true thickness not determinable) of *Orusia* Shales resting with slight discordance on Middle Cambrian rocks. A number of excavations made by Cobbold N. of the Comley–Shootrough road found shales which were assigned to the *Orusia* horizon.

The Black Shales have not been recorded from the Comley area although they were described by Stubblefield (1930b, p. 54) from the Bentleyford Brook, 2½ miles N.E. of Comley.

The Shineton Shales are poorly exposed but a stream section [48969669] 370 yd at 336° from Shootrough shows striped grey silty shale with fossils of the Tremadoc Series.

5/ORDOVICIAN: CARADOC SERIES

Ordovician rocks occur in the S.E. part of the area covered by the geological map, in two main outcrops separated by the Uriconian rocks of the Hope Bowdler and Cardington hills. The succession in the vertical section of the map shows that only part of the Ordovician, the Caradoc Series, occurs in the Church Stretton area. In the Shelve area, W. of the Long Mynd, the Arenig, Llanvirn and Llandeilo series underlie the Caradoc while in other parts of the country the Ashgill Series occurs above the Caradoc. The rocks of the Church Stretton area are mainly shallow-water sandstones and siltstones with a shelly fauna, locally so abundant as to form thin limestones. They were probably deposited in a shelf area which was relatively stable and was not submerged until Caradoc times, in contrast to a more rapidly subsiding basin which extended into Wales from W. of the Long Mynd, and in which deposition took place throughout the earlier part of the Ordovician period.

The subdivisions of the shaly rocks of the basin facies are based upon graptolite faunas, the zones recognized in the Caradoc Series of Wales being those of *Nemagraptus gracilis*, *Diplograptus multidens*, *Dicranograptus clingani* and *Pleurograptus linearis*. The shelf rocks of the Church Stretton area mostly contain shelly fossils with very few graptolites but a few specimens have been found in the coarse deposits, making possible a correlation between the shallow and deeper water faunas. Thus Stubblefield (1930a, p. 87) identified *N. gracilis* (Hall) in specimens collected from the Hoar Edge Grit and Bulman (1948, p. 227) discovered *Diplograptus multidens* Elles and Wood in the Harnage Shales of Coundmoor Brook, about 6 miles N.E. of Church Stretton. Dean (1958, p. 226) discussed the correlation of the shelly and graptolitic faunas concluding that all the beds above the Chatwall Flags could probably be assigned to the *Dicranograptus clingani* Zone and that there was no acceptable evidence of the presence of the *P. linearis* Zone in south Shropshire.

The lithological classification used in this account follows that of the Church Stretton Memoir (1968) which is broadly the same as that introduced by Lapworth (1916, p. 38) for the Caradoc area; the historical development of this classification was described by Dean (1958).

The palaeontological classification of the Caradoc Series is based on the work of B. B. Bancroft who, in a series of papers published between 1928 and 1949, developed a system dependent on his recognition of a succession of distinctive brachiopod–trilobite faunas. The Series was divided into seven stages to which local geographical names were applied and which were related to lithological divisions. Dean (1958) amplified Bancroft's work and made a new correlation between the shelly and graptolitic faunas. He showed (1958 and 1960) that in the Soudley [477917] area there is a slight stratigraphical break between the *alternata* Limestone and the Chatwall Flags. No major diachronism was observed in the beds above the Chatwall Sandstone, but at Soudley sandstone occurs at a lower horizon in the Chatwall group than elsewhere and the base of the underlying Chatwall Flags is at a lower horizon in the N.E. than the S.W. The basal Ordovician rocks in the Hope Bowdler area are younger than elsewhere and are strongly diachronous over an irregular floor of Pre-Cambrian and Cambrian rocks.

Although some of the lithological units shown on the map are diachronous, in so far as they are units, they constitute a classification which is useful to the layman and the geologist in the field. Table 1 relates the palaeontological classifications to Dean's lithological units and those used in this account; it is based largely on Dean's work (1958, figs. 3 and 4).

Hoar Edge Grit

The Hoar Edge Grit is named from its outcrop along the well-marked ridge of Hoar Edge which extends N.E. from Shootrough [491964]. Other small outcrops, some of them

Table 1

Graptolite Zone	Stage	Lithological Succession — Dean — Soudley area (Upper Llandovery)	Lithological Succession — Dean — The Cwms–Willstone	Geological Survey
Dicranograptus clingani	Onnian	? Onnia Beds	? Onnia Beds	Onny Shales
	Actonian	Grey mudstones of Ticklerton	Yellow sandstones = Acton Scott Beds	Acton Scott Group
	Marshbrookian (Upper) / Upper Longvillian (Lower)	Cheney Longville Flags (Upper / Lower)	Cheney Longville Flags	Cheney Longville Flags
		alternata Limestone	*alternata* Limestone	*alternata* Limestone
	Lower Longvillian	Faunal Break	Upper Chatwall Sandstone	Chatwall Sandstone
Diplograptus multidens	Soudleyan	Soudley Sandstone / ?	Lower Chatwall Sandstone	Chatwall Flags
	Harnagian	Harnage Shales	? Shales	Harnage Shales
Nemagraptus gracilis	Costonian	Uriconian	'Hoar Edge Grits' of the Cwms	Hoar Edge Grit
			Longmyndian or Cambrian	

fault-bounded, occur in the vicinity of Cwms Plantation [480947], within the Church Stretton Fault Complex. The Grit rests unconformably on possible Wentnor Series rocks near Cwms Farm [476941] and on Lower, Middle or Upper Cambrian rocks at other localities. In the area [476945] 700 yd N.N.E. of Cwms Farm, two small faults in Cambrian rocks apparently pass under the unconformable Grit, indicating that there was some small-scale faulting in the Cambrian prior to the deposition of the Caradoc Series.

The Hoar Edge Grit is a coarse sandstone up to about 150 ft thick, with well rounded grains, pebbly at the base and usually pale grey or white. Some beds are feldspathic with pink or white grains of feldspar, while in the pebbly layers the pebbles are mainly of quartz with some of igneous rock, probably of Uriconian origin. Brachiopods, including *Dinorthis* cf. *flabellulum* (J. de C. Sowerby) and *Salopia salteri* (Davidson), have been found at two exposures [48279511 and 48439520] close to the bridle road from Willstone to the Cwms.

In the Harnage–Cressage area N.E. of the area of the map, Dean (1958) recognized a three-fold subdivision of the Grit:

Rhynchonellid Grits.
Sandy limestones with *Harknessella subquadrata* Bancroft.
Sandy shales and limestones with *Harknessella subplicata* Bancroft.

He pointed out that the Rhynchonellid Grits are Harnagian and that in the Cwms area the Hoar Edge Grit includes these beds and the underlying beds with *H. subquadrata*. The fauna of the latter beds shows certain Harnagian elements which led Dean to the conclusion that no important faunal break occurs at this level, as postulated by Robertson (*in* Pocock and others 1938, p. 86).

Harnage Shales

There are small outcrops of the Harnage Shales within the Church Stretton Fault Complex near the S. end of Ragleth Hill [446914], in the vicinity of Cwms Plantation [479948] and to the N. East of F3 an unconformable cover of Harnage Shales forms the S. limit of the Uriconian outcrop between

Dryhill [460924] and Gutter Farm [498931] while N. of the Sharpstones Thrust the Shales form a vale W. of the Chatwall Sandstone ridge. South of Cardington Hill they are largely grey and brown shales and silty mudstones between about 200 and 400 ft thick, with calcareous pebbly grits and sandstones at the base and thin bands of grit or flags locally at higher levels. North of the Sharpstones Thrust the Shales are mainly grey or greenish mudstones, commonly shaly, up to about 800 ft thick and with bands of sandstone at some horizons.

In general the Harnage Shales are poorly exposed because of their relatively soft character and sections are found mainly in streams and quarries. In a small quarry [44549136] near the S. end of Ragleth Hill, steeply dipping grits, probably of the Wentnor Series, occur in the floor and are overlain in the E. part of the quarry by a calcareous gritty sandstone with some pebbles, which is the basal part of the Harnage Shales. The pebbles include quartz, and pink and green fragments, probably Uriconian rocks. The basal sandstone passes up into grey and brown calcareous shaly mudstones which form the bulk of the Harnage sediments.

In the Hope Bowdler area, a quarry [46309244] shows fissures up to about 6 in wide in Uriconian rocks, filled with sandy mudstone which was found by Strachan and others (1948, p. 276) to be richly fossiliferous and of Harnagian age. Closer to Hope Bowdler, a section [47399244] at the side of the Church Stretton road shows fossiliferous Harnage Shales with a 1-ft basal band of conglomerate resting upon Uriconian tuff. The fauna includes the brachiopods *Dalmanella sp.* and *Glyptorthis sp.* and the trilobites *Broeggerolithus* cf. *harnagensis* (Bancroft) and *Salterolithus sp.* A comparable section occurs at Upper House [47529258] where the Harnage basal conglomerate is about 2 ft thick and contains Uriconian fragments up to about 1½ in across. East of the village the base of the Shales is exposed in a stream [49019304] at Gutter Cottage and other sections occur in the stream about 300 yd and 700 yd downstream from the cottage.

In the syncline at Cwms Plantation [480946] there are small exposures of the Harnage Shales at [47699477] and [47749433] while in the outcrop E. of F3 the Shales are exposed in stream sections at [48239479] and [49529642].

Near the E. limit of the area [498944], S. of the Hill End Thrust, the presence of a fault-bounded outcrop of Harnage Shales has been inferred from the occurrence nearby [49949431] of a green shelly sandstone with a fauna probably belonging to the Chatwall Flags.

Chatwall Flags

To the S. of Hope Bowdler and N.E. of the Sharpstones Thrust, the outcrop of the Chatwall Flags lies S.E. of that of the Harnage Shales and forms the lower part of the scarp feature made by the overlying Chatwall Sandstone. South of Little Stretton there are a number of smaller outcrops, partly fault-bounded, within the Church Stretton Fault Complex. The rocks S. of Hope Bowdler are mainly flaggy micaceous sandstones, brown or green and commonly with crinoid columnals; they vary in thickness between 75 and 225 ft. North of the Cardington hills the Flags are up to 300 ft thick and consist of yellow flaggy sandstones and sandy mudstones with lenses of impure limestone and bands of crinoid columnals. There is a small outlier of Chatwall Flags in the axial region of a syncline, [480946] at Cwms Plantation.

Exposures in the Chatwall Flags are generally poor and scattered, but sections have been examined in an old quarry [44509112] W. of The Hough, in a stream [46129140] W. of Chelmick and in a lane [48589512] W. of Willstone. The last locality has yielded specimens of the brachiopods *Macrocoelia* [*Rafinesquina*] *expansa* (J. de C. Sowerby) and *Sowerbyella sp.* and the trilobite *Broeggerolithus* cf. *broeggeri* (Bancroft).

Chatwall Sandstone

South of Little Stretton there are small outcrops of Chatwall Sandstone within the Church Stretton Fault Complex from the Marshbrook valley [44069054] towards The Hough [44969128]. South of Hope Bowdler the Sandstone forms an escarpment from S.W. of Chelmick [46009100] to E. of Common Farm [49909274], and N. of Willstone Hill it gives rise to a prominent feature extending from E. of Cwms Plantation [48509458] to Folly Bank [49739620]. In the railway cutting [44069054] N. of Marshbrook mill there is a section through about 55 ft of the Chatwall Sandstone which is a massive grey, purplish or brown sandstone with occasional thin bands of shelly fossils and with thin bands of shelly limestone in the top 10 ft. The fauna from this exposure includes the polyzoan *Mesotrypa lens* (McCoy), the brachiopods *Dalmanella lepta* (Bancroft) and *Sowerbyella soudleyensis* Jones and the trilobite *Broeggerolithus nicholsoni* (Reed). South of Hope Bowdler the Sandstone is known locally as the Soudley Sandstone and is well exposed in Soudley Quarry [47729182] which shows the top 20 ft of the group. These comprise purple and greenish brown sandstone, locally conspicuously colour-banded with thin bands rich in crinoid columnals and other shelly fossils including the brachiopods *Bicuspina sp.* and *Macrocoelia expansa*. The rock is a readily worked freestone which has been widely used as a building stone in the district. North of Willstone Hill purple sandstone is exposed in a quarry [48699512] S.W. of Willstone and fossiliferous beds occur in an old quarry [48989562] N.N.W. of Willstone where the brachiopods *Kjaerina* cf. *jonesi* Bancroft and *Sowerbyella soudleyensis* have been found. Close to Folly Bank cross roads [49739620] there are small exposures of yellow sandstone in the lane leading to Willstone and in a small quarry 50 yd E. of the cross roads. East of the area of the map the Sandstone is a greenish grey and purple argillaceous sandstone with bands containing small pebbles of quartz, quartzite and grit. It attains a thickness of about 300 ft on Yell Bank [506970].

Bancroft (1929, p. 40) showed that at Soudley, the Chatwall (Soudley) Sandstone belonged to the Soudleyan Stage and the *alternata* Limestone to the Upper Longvillian, there being no rocks corresponding to the Lower Longvillian Stage. Thus at Soudley the Sandstone is older than at Chatwall to the N.E. or in the Onny valley to the S.W.

alternata **Limestone**

The *alternata* Limestone occurs at the base of the Cheney Longville Flags with which it is grouped. It is mapped separately only N. of Willstone Hill where it may be up to about 20–30 ft thick. In the outcrops S. of Hope Bowdler it is not sufficiently distinctive to be mapped separately. The Limestone consists of a succession of lenticular shelly limestones characterized by an abundance of *Heterorthis alternata* (J. de C. Sowerby) accompanied by other brachiopods and trilobites. The limestone lenticles are up to 2 ft thick and are interbedded with green micaceous flags and shales which are also highly fossiliferous.

In the Marshbrook railway cutting [44059052] the *alternata* Limestone overlies the Chatwall Sandstone and is represented by 44 ft of buff siltstone with shelly limestone in bands up to 1 ft thick. These beds have yielded the brachiopods *Bancroftina sp.*, *Sowerbyella sericea* (J. de C. Sowerby), the scaphopod-like *Tentaculites sp.* and the trilobites *Brongniartella bisulcata* (McCoy) and *Kloucekia apiculata* (McCoy). The Limestone crops out in the lane [46619154] N.W. of Chelmick and is also exposed in the upper part of Soudley Quarry [47729182] where it consists only of 3 ft of green mudstone with three bands of shelly limestone 4–5 in thick, which contain the brachiopods *Dalmanella sp.*, *Kjaerina bipartita* (Salter), *Sowerbyella sericea*, *Strophomena grandis* (J. de C. Sowerby) and the trilobites *Broeggerolithus* cf. *longiceps* (Bancroft), *Brongniartella bisulcata* and *Kloucekia apiculata*. North of Willstone Hill the Limestone occurs in an old quarry [48989562] N.N.W. of Willstone, and has been traced to the N.E. by small exposures and soil debris to Folly Bank near which there is another poor exposure [49909626].

Bancroft's (1933) recognition of a non-sequence below the *alternata* Limestone and his placing of the Limestone at the base of the Upper Longvillian Stage, was supported by the work of Dean (1958, pp. 220–2) which showed that the fauna of the Limestone has more in common with the Upper rather than the Lower Longvillian. Consequently the *alternata* Limestone is now grouped with the Cheney Longville Flags rather than with the Chatwall Sandstone, which was the practice adopted by the authors of the Shrewsbury Memoir.

Cheney Longville Flags

The Cheney Longville Flags together with the *alternata* Limestone make up the Upper Longvillian and Marshbrookian stages of Bancroft. The rocks are predominantly yellowish-weathering, greenish grey flags with interbedded shales and rubbly siltstones. Thin beds of fine-grained massive sandstone occur and thin shelly limestones, usually decalcified, are quite common. Brachiopods and trilobites are common throughout the formation and amongst other fossils which occur, the most conspicuous and characteristic is *Tentaculites*. Over most of the outcrop the Flags are about 400 ft thick but they are up to 600 ft thick in the Cardington area N. of Willstone Hill.

South of Little Stretton there are a number of outcrops, fault-bounded in part, of the Cheney Longville Flags which overlie the Chatwall Sandstone within the Church Stretton Fault Complex. From Oakwood [446903] to N. of Ragdon [458915] there is a larger outcrop, largely fault-bounded but succeeded to the S.E. by the Acton Scott Group. The main outcrop of the Flags forms the dip slope S.E. of the Chatwall Sandstone scarp and extends from near Swiss Cottage [450900] to N. of Peartree [498927] where it is cut out by an unconformable cover of *Pentamerus* Beds. North of Willstone Hill the outcrop of the flags lies S.E. of that of the *alternata* Limestone and in this area dips are steep and probably locally overturned to the N.W. as a result of faulting.

About 16 ft of buff flags and sandstones, low in the Marshbrookian Stage, with the brachiopods *Dalmanella wattsi* (Bancroft), *Nicolella sp.*, *Strophomena grandis* and the trilobite *Brongniartella bisulcata* are exposed at the roadside [43989002] S. of Marshbrook mill. The Flags cap the wooded slope which trends N.E. from the main road [442908] toward The Hough and are exposed at [44519094]. They are well exposed in the stream section [45069066] S. of The Hough and are also seen in a number of small exposures around Ragdon [485915]. On the E. side of Rag Batch [45979089 and 46099100] two exposures of brown flaggy sandstone and shale have yielded a fauna indicative of a low horizon in the Flags. There are many outcrops of flags and flaggy mudstone around Chelmick [468914] and a section in the stream [46759101] S. of Chelmick has yielded a Marshbrookian fauna which includes the polyzoan '*Favosites fibrilla*' Smith and the brachiopods *Dalmanella wattsi, Sower-*

byella sp. and *Strophomena grandis.* At Soudley Quarry [47729182] the lowest part of the Flags is exposed above the *alternata* Limestone and consists of 15 ft of banded sandstone, siltstone and silty mudstone with a 4-in shell bed 7 ft 6 in above the base. This part of the quarry section has yielded the brachiopods *Sowerbyella sericea* and *Strophomena grandis* and the trilobites *Broeggerolithus* cf. *longiceps, Brongniartella sp.* and *Kloucekia apiculata.* There are more exposures in the valley below the fish ponds at Soudley [478915]. At Hollies [48459176] there are exposures of flaggy mudstone with shelly bands containing a Marshbrookian fauna. This exposure is celebrated for the controversy about the age of the fossils obtained from there (Cobbold 1900, p. 37). The house, built on Caradoc rocks, adjoined a lime-kiln built of the same material but in which Silurian *Pentamerus* Beds, from a short distance to the S.E., were burnt. The calcined remains of both rocks furnished a 'mixed' fauna reputed to come from the exposure at Hollies. Between Willstone Hill and Willstone the Cheney Longville Flags are steeply dipping and apparently overturned with dips of up to 62° to the N.W. in the lane [48909520] W. of Willstone. These steep dips may be associated with movements on fault F3 of the Church Stretton Complex to the W. and on a parallel strike fault trending S.S.W. from Willstone. South of Folly Bank the Flags from a south-facing dip slope which extends N.E. from Willstone.

Acton Scott Group

The Acton Scott Group forms the Actonian Stage of Bancroft and occurs in two outcrops on the southern boundary of the area and also in an outcrop N. of Cardington Hill. In the southern outcrops the rocks are olive-green and grey silty mudstones and siltstones in which is developed an 80-ft lens of sandy limestone at Acton Scott [455895] just S. of the area of the map. The thickness of the group reaches about 200 ft in the vicinity of Acton Scott. North of Cardington Hill the Group may be about 500 ft thick and consists of yellowish shales and mudstones which include two beds of flaggy, shelly sandstone, the lower about 50 ft and the upper about 70 ft thick.

East and N.E. of Oakwood [446903] there is an outcrop of the Acton Scott Group which conformably overlies the Cheney Longville Flags to the N.W. but is limited to the S.E. by a strike fault trending N.E. from Swiss Cottage [449900]. In the stream [44969025] N. of Swiss Cottage there are small exposures of shaly siltstone and mudstone dipping N.N.W. at about 30°. Farther north in the same stream [45059053] there is a section in the lowest part of the Group showing buff or green shaly, silty and micaceous mudstones with occasional calcareous bands up to 6 in thick. These beds contain the brachiopods *Cryptothyris para-cyclica* (Bancroft), *Leptaena sp.* and *Onniella sp.* and the trilobite *Otarion sp.* An outcrop of the Acton Scott Group trends N.E. from Hatton [468903] to the Soudley–Ticklerton road [481912], near which it is cut out as a result of overstep by the *Pentamerus* Beds. There is a section in the stream bank [46459013] by the road bridge S.W. of Hatton, showing 24 ft of grey micaceous silty mudstone with bands of grey limestone; the fauna indicates a horizon in the lower part of the Group and includes the brachiopods *Onniella* cf. *grandis* Bancroft and *Reuschella semiglobata* Bancroft and the trilobites *Chasmops extensa* (Boeck) and *Onnicalymene laticeps* (Bancroft). At Hatton [46869036] 8 ft of buff flaggy siltstone and sandstone are exposed in a farm yard on the N. side of the road. These beds, in the higher part of the Group, form the small ridge on which the village of Hatton stands. In two stream sections [47929104, 48079116] N.W. of Ticklerton there are exposures of grey mudstone with shelly bands dipping S.E. at 15–20°.

North of Cardington Hill the lower beds of the Acton Scott Group lie S. of the dip slope of the Cheney Longville Flags. They are thought to be mainly shales but are very poorly exposed so that little is known of them, and their thickness, possibly 300 ft, is only an estimate. The lowest sandstone in the Group is about 50 ft thick and forms a feature which trends eastwards from Willstone [492952], where it is cut off to the W. by a N.E.–S.W. fault. In the Willstone farm yard [49209523] there is a section at the base of the sandstone, in 14 ft of yellow sandy and silty flagstones, dipping S. at 30°. The sandstone ridge is bounded to the S. by a hollow, thought to be occupied by shales, estimated to be about 60 ft thick, which are not exposed in the area of the map. South of these shales is a second ridge formed by the higher of the two sandstones. It is not exposed W. of Cardington and has been mapped only from the feature. It is considered to be cut off to the W. by the N.E.–S.W. fault at Willstone and to the S.E. by the Hill End Thrust. The ground between this sandstone feature and the Uriconian rocks of Cardington Hill is thought to be occupied by argillaceous rocks in the upper part of the Acton Scott Group. There are, however, no exposures of these beds.

Onny Shales

The Onny Shales form a very small outcrop on the map [46749000] south of Hatton, which is the northern limit of a larger outcrop extending S.W. to Cheney Longville [420850]. The rocks are unconformably overlain by the Silurian *Pentamerus* Beds, there are no exposures within the area of the map and they are best seen farther south, in the Onny valley section [425853]. The rocks are mainly grey and buff micaceous siltstones and mudstones not easily distinguishable from the rocks of the underlying Acton Scott Group, from which they have been differentiated mainly on palaeontological grounds. They contain numerous Trinucleid trilobites, including *Onnia superba* (Bancroft), which are almost unknown in the Acton Scott Group. The Onny Shales are the equivalent of the Onnian Stage of Bancroft (1933) and the *Onnia* Beds of Dean (1958, p. 213).

6/SILURIAN

Silurian rocks occur in the S. part of the area around Ticklerton [483907], in the Minton [431906] area and in the Church Stretton valley. The stratigraphical sequence is shown on the vertical section on the map. In the Ticklerton area the *Pentamerus* Beds dip gently eastwards and rest unconformably on Ordovician rocks to the W. They are succeeded to the S.E. by the Hughley Shales and the Wenlock Shales. In the Minton area the Silurian sequence ranges from the basal grit and conglomerate of Upper Llandovery age to the Wenlock Shales. Here there is some repetition of outcrops due to movements on faults of the Church Stretton Complex and associated faults. The All Stretton outcrop is bounded to the S.E. by fault F1 and only the beds above the Wenlock Shales are exposed on the slopes W. of Caer Caradoc. The *Pentamerus* Beds, Hughley Shales and Wenlock Shales are covered by the drift deposits in the bottom of the valley and are known from two Geological Survey boreholes [45719447 and 47359653], from temporary trench excavations on the N. side of Church Stretton and from a borehole [44769236] near Brockhurst Castle put down on behalf of Birmingham University Geology Department. Professor F. W. Shotton has kindly provided information that this last borehole found Hughley Shales at a depth of 117 ft below boulder clay and gravel. The map and horizontal section indicate that the *Pentamerus* Beds rest unconformably on the Longmyndian, which was the suggestion made by Cobbold (1892). However, the N.W. limit of the Silurian has not been precisely determined because of the absence of exposures and it is possible that the All Stretton outcrop is continuous with the Silurian at Little Stretton in the low ground E. of Brockhurst Hill [448925]. Similarly the extent of the Silurian outcrop in the vicinity of Gorseybank [471968] is not known with any certainty.

In Silurian, as in Ordovician times the Church Stretton area was situated marginally between a relatively shallow shelf sea to the S.E. and a deep-water basin to the N.W. Although the boundary between the two areas lay in the general region of the Church Stretton Fault Complex it must be considered as a diffuse zone rather than a sharp boundary along the line of the Complex. The oldest Silurian rocks in the area do not exhibit a contrast between shelf and basin facies. They rest with unconformity on Ordovician and older rocks and were laid down as the earliest deposits of a transgressive sea which did not reach the Church Stretton area until Upper Llandovery times. South-west of Little Stretton the basal deposits exhibit a marginal shore-line facies with such features as pebble banks and sea stacks but elsewhere they are of finer grain size and comprise siltstones and mudstones. By the close of Upper Llandovery times there was deposition of fine-grained sediment throughout the area.

A difference between graptolitic basin deposits and shelly shelf rocks is first apparent in the upper part of the Wenlock Series. There is a marked contrast between the shallow-water reef limestones of Wenlock Edge, 6 miles E. of Church Stretton and the graptolitic shales of the same age in the Long Mountain area, about 15 miles to the N.W. Whittard (1952, p. 170–1) and Dineley (1960, p. 101–2) considered that the facies change took place across the Church Stretton Fault Complex with an intermediate facies occurring at Brokenstones [420880] within the Complex. However the work of Dean (1964, p. 285) and the Geological Survey (Greig and others 1968, p. 143) indicates that the westward change of facies in the Wenlock Series, S. of the Long Mynd, is more gradual. The Wenlock sediments of the Clungunford [400790] and Edgton [385858] areas, E. and W. of the Fault Complex respectively, are essentially similar and consist of siltstones with a mixed graptolite and trilobite fauna with nodular limestones in the higher beds. This sequence can be taken as intermediate between the shelly facies of Much Wenlock and the graptolitic facies of the Long Mountain.

The distribution of sedimentary facies in the Ludlow Series of the Welsh Borders was discussed by Holland and Lawson (1963) who concluded that the margin between the shelf and basin facies was not a straight line such as the Church Stretton Fault Complex, but was curved and convex to the east. In addition, the position of the boundary fluctuated considerably in Ludlow times. In the Upper Ludlow rocks there is no distinction between shelf and basin facies although the thickness of the sediments (calcareous shelly siltstones) increases towards the west. This uniformity in the highest Silurian rocks heralds the great palaeogeographical changes which were to follow in the Old Red Sandstone (Devonian) Period.

Upper Llandovery Series

The division of the Upper Llandovery rocks into *Pentamerus* Beds and Hughley (Purple) Shales follows the practice of Whittard (1932) who also subdivided the *Pentamerus* Beds into a basal arenaceous phase overlain by a mudstone phase. The subdivision on the map into basal grit and conglomerate and shales and limestones corresponds to the two phases recognized by Whittard. From a study of the graptolites, found in what is essentially a shelly fauna, Whittard (1932, p. 885) concluded that the *Pentamerus* Beds and Hughley Shales were the equivalents of the Upper Llandovery graptolite zones of *Monograptus turriculatus* and *M. crispus*.

PENTAMERUS BEDS

Minton area

On the S.E. side of the Long Mynd there are outcrops of the basal grits and conglomerates, lying with strong unconformity on the Longmyndian. The rocks comprise rather massive grey and purple sandstone and grit, locally pebbly and conglomeratic with a south-easterly dip varying from about 20° to 60°. There are exposures of conglomerate on both sides of the mouths of Minton Batch [42219006, 42449020] and Callow Hollow [43109096, 43309120] and on the spur [44229196] N.W. of Little Stretton. At the last locality there is a small excavation showing purple sandy conglomerate overlain by a 3-ft layer composed of roughly bedded thin pebbles of grey shale, probably derived from the adjacent Stretton Shale Group (Longmyndian). West of

Marshbrook mill [439902] there are small exposures and debris of grit and conglomerate which rest unconformably on Ordovician rocks to the E. About 600 yd to the S.W., by New House Farm [436899], there are more extensive exposures of pebbly grit which dips N.N.W. at about 45°. This outcrop lies E. of fault F1 of the Church Stretton Complex. At Hamperley [42178912] 1 mile S.W. of Minton, a Geological Survey borehole proved 158 ft of sandstone and conglomerate resting unconformably on Pre-Cambrian rocks. This evidence shows that the marginal gritty beds extend for at least 800 yd S.E. of the present margin of the Long Mynd.

The shale and limestone facies of the *Pentamerus* Beds probably occurs in a number of narrow outcrops S.E. of the basal grits but is not exposed in the Minton area. From several small exposures in the overlying Hughley and Wenlock shales it is considered that the Minton outcrop of the Silurian is affected by a number of faults, mainly strike faults, and it appears that the outcrops of the *Pentamerus* Beds above the basal grits are bounded to the S.E. by faults. From better exposed areas elsewhere the upper part of the *Pentamerus* Beds is known to consist of grey shaly siltstones and mudstones with pale grey sandy limestones, usually less than 3 in thick but occasionally up to 1 ft in thickness. The characteristic brachiopod *Pentamerus oblongus* J. de C. Sowerby is abundant in most of the limestones and locally in the siltstones. West of Marshbrook mill the outcrop of basal grit and conglomerate, dipping N.N.W., is bounded to the W. by an outcrop of the shale and limestone facies. This is not exposed within the area of the map but there is a small section in a stream [43428983] 200 yd S.W. of New House Farm, showing green mudstone with thin bands of fossiliferous limestone which have yielded the brachiopods '*Camarotoechia*' *nucula* (J. de C. Sowerby) and *Leptostrophia sp.*

Ticklerton area

In the Silurian outcrop E. of the Church Stretton Fault Complex the basal grit (known as the Kenley Grit) does not crop out in the area of the map and is known only to the N.E. of Plaish [530960]. South-west of this locality the grit outcrop is cut out by overstep of the overlying shales and limestones which, in the Ticklerton area rest unconformably on the Chatwall Flags and Sandstone, Cheney Longville Flags, Acton Scott Beds and Onny Shales. The *Pentamerus* Beds of this area dip S.E. at about 20° and are similar to the shale and limestone facies of the Minton outcrops. In a stream [482909] N.W. of Ticklerton there are exposures of grey silty mudstones with bands of flaggy micaceous sandstone and beds of limestone packed with *Pentamerus oblongus* well known by the classic name of 'Government Rock' which derives from the arrow mark formed by the internal structures of the shell seen in cross section. There are poor exposures of brown shaly mudstone in a stream [495919] S. of Hargrove Farm.

All Stretton area

In this area the *Pentamerus* Beds are nowhere exposed and are known only from a Geological Survey borehole at Springbank Farm [45719447] which proved 140 ft of the shale and limestone facies resting unconformably on the Longmyndian. Scattered fragments of grey shale were found in the basal 6 in but there was no development of the basal grit and conglomerate of the Minton area.

HUGHLEY SHALES

The Hughley Shales take their name from the hamlet of Hughley [565980] which is situated on the main Silurian outcrop in the Shrewsbury District (Pocock and others, 1938). These are the Purple Shales of Whittard (1932) and consist of purple and maroon shaly mudstones, locally silty with many green bands and patches. Thin calcareous laminae are common and thin bands of shelly and argillaceous limestone occur locally.

Minton area

The Silurian of this area is poorly exposed and the faulted repetition of outcrops of Hughley Shales and Wenlock Shales, shown on the map must be regarded as conjectural.

The boundaries are based on a few poor exposures and on information kindly provided by the late Professor W. F. Whittard who dug a number of trial excavations in the course of his investigations in the area (Whittard 1932). There is a small exposure of weathered purple shale at the roadside [42629028] S.W. of Minton which signifies the proximity of the Hughley Shales at this locality to the gritty *Pentamerus* Beds and the Longmyndian. The greater part of the shale and limestone facies of the *Pentamerus* Beds is considered to be cut out by a fault. Other poor exposures of the Hughley Shales occur in a farm track [43409056] S.E. of Minton and in a deep ditch [44009160] S.W. of Little Stretton. Hughley Shales were found below 117 ft of drift in a borehole [44769236] near Brockhurst Castle (see p. 51).

Ticklerton area

Purple and grey shales with thin siltstone bands are exposed in a stream [47719006, 47949005] E. of Hatton and there is a small exposure of purple shale at Ticklerton [486906]. In a stream section [49549186] there are poor exposures of grey shaly mudstone close to the base of the Hughley Shales.

All Stretton area

Like the *Pentamerus* Beds, the Hughley Shales are not exposed in the All Stretton area and are known only from the Springbank Farm borehole [45719447] which proved about 120 ft of the lower part of the Shales overlying the *Pentamerus* Beds. The borehole was situated within the outcrop of the Shales and did not penetrate the higher beds.

Wenlock Series

The Wenlock Series comprises the Wenlock Shales which are overlain by the Wenlock Limestone. In the main Silurian outcrop of Wenlock Edge the Tickwood Beds, originally described by Davidson and Maw (1881, p. 102), have been recognized below the Wenlock Limestone. This group of nodular limestones and siltstones was considered by Hains and Hoare (*in* Greig and others 1968, p. 153) to be transitional between the Wenlock Shales and the Wenlock Limestone. Within the area of the 1:25 000 geological map the Tickwood Beds have not been mapped separately although part of the Wenlock Limestone outcrop in the All Stretton area is of Tickwood Beds lithology. In the Minton and Ticklerton areas the Wenlock Shales have been separated from the Hughley Shales mainly on the basis of an upward colour change from purple to grey. In the Plowden area [380880] to the S.W., Whittard (1932, p. 869) noted that the lowest 40 ft of the Wenlock Shales consisted of interbedded grey and purple shales which could have been mistaken for Hughley Shales but for their Wenlockian fauna. Basal purple Wenlock Shales have not been identified in the Minton, Ticklerton or All Stretton outcrops.

WENLOCK SHALES

Minton area

In this area there are two outcrops of Wenlock Shales which result from repetition by strike faulting, the more easterly outcrop being bounded on its E. side by F1 of the Church Stretton Fault Complex. The boundaries are conjectural and are based on a few scattered exposures, the area being largely covered by drift. In the neighbourhood of Minton, green siltstone was seen in a temporary exposure at [43109046] and greenish grey shale was found in a water borehole [43089060] drilled in the village. In a sunken lane [43189078] N. of the village there is a section in fossiliferous grey micaceous siltstone which appears to be steeply folded. This section has yielded the trilobite *Calymene blumenbachii* Brongniart and the graptolite *Monograptus* cf. *priodon* (Bronn). The late Professor W. F. Whittard (personal communication) found evidence of the Wenlock Shales in the fields immediately N.E. of this exposure. In the easterly outcrop of the Shales grey micaceous shale was seen in the valley [43389008] S.S.E. of Minton and greenish shale with limestone nodules was formerly worked in a small pit [43649043] W. of Marshbrook mill. South-west of Little Stretton there is debris of siltstone, probably from the Wenlock Shales on the low hill [44099135] W. of the alluvium.

Ticklerton area

The Wenlock Shales of this area occupy low ground largely covered by boulder clay but there are some exposures in the valley S. of Ticklerton. Grey silty mudstone with calcareous nodules, near the base of the Shales, is exposed in a stream section [48229008], and in the old brick pits [48559042] S.E. of Ticklerton there is a section in 12 ft of calcareous grey mudstone with bands of fossiliferous limestone nodules.

All Stretton area

The outcrop of the Wenlock Shales probably covers a broad strip of the drift-covered ground N.W. of the Church Stretton bypass but there are no exposures of these rocks. Temporary trench exposures revealed fossiliferous beds in 1904 at [45699409] N.E. of Church Stretton, in 1929 in Essex Road, Church Stretton [45659385, 45639385], and more recently (1963) sewer trench excavations uncovered greenish grey shales in the same area [45659416, 45739394] (information from the late Mr. T. H. Whitehead). The only other record of Wenlock Shales from the All Stretton outcrop is from a Geological Survey borehole [47359653] near Botvyle which proved 366 ft of the Shales beneath the Upper Coal Measures, the junction between these two formations probably being faulted. This borehole did not reach the base of the Wenlock Shales.

WENLOCK LIMESTONE

The Wenlock Limestone occurs only in the All Stretton area and crops out E. of the Church Stretton bypass on the slopes below Caer Caradoc. The mapped outcrop probably includes equivalents of the Tickwood Beds and the Wenlock Limestone of Wenlock Edge but most of the exposures are in the lower part of the Limestone and consist of interbedded limestone and calcareous shale, similar to the Tickwood Beds. At its southern end the outcrop is probably cut off by the fault F1 and the most southerly exposure [46089408], in a coppice E. of the bypass, shows vertical calcareous shaly mudstone with calcareous nodules passing eastwards into impure nodular limestone. The fauna from these beds includes the brachiopods *Atrypa reticularis* (Linné), *Brachyprion arenaceus* (Davidson), '*Camarotoechia*' *nucula*, '*Chonetes lepisma*' (J. de C. Sowerby), *Craniops implicata* (J. de C. Sowerby) and *Eospirifer radiatus* (J. de C. Sowerby). The outcrop has been traced northwards from topographical features and is apparently displaced along several small faults. In Hough Coppice [46839545, 46969566] E. of All Stretton there are poor exposures of interbedded limestone and calcareous shale dipping E.S.E. at about 35°. The Wenlock Limestone outcrop is apparently cut off by a fault trending W.N.W.–E.S.E., north of Hough Coppice.

Ludlow Series

Rocks of the Ludlow Series occur only in the All Stretton area and have been divided into the Lower Ludlow Shales, Aymestry Group and Upper Ludlow Shales, in accordance with the divisions mapped in the main Silurian outcrop E. of Wenlock Edge (Greig and others 1968, p. 156). South of a W.N.W.–E.S.E. fault at [472957] the Lower Ludlow Shales and Aymestry Group overlie the Wenlock Limestone and dip E. towards fault F1 of the Church Stretton Complex. North of the W.N.W.–E.S.E. fault there is a marked swing in strike, and exposures in the Aymestry Group S. of Botvyle show that the rocks there dip steeply to the south. The limits of the fault-bounded area of Lower Ludlow Shales N.E. of Botvyle are conjectural because of an extensive cover of boulder clay.

LOWER LUDLOW SHALES

Calcareous shale dipping E. at 27°, is exposed in a stream [46699502] S.E. of All Stretton and has yielded the brachiopods *Chonetoidea grayi* (Davidson) and *Leptaena rhomboidalis* (Wilckens) and the graptolites *Monograptus colonus* (Barrande) *M. colonus compactus* Wood and *M.* cf. *varians* Wood. There are no exposures of the Shales in the outcrop E. of Hough Coppice [471955] but S.S.W. of Botvyle [47529596] there is a section showing grey calcareous shales with limestone nodules dipping S. at 10°. Immediately N. of Botvyle there was formerly an exposure in a pond [47679620] (now obscured) showing green and grey mudstone with limestone nodules, with patchy purple staining, which yielded a fauna of probable Lower Ludlow age.

AYMESTRY GROUP

The Aymestry Group is represented by about 200 ft of nodular limestones with bands of calcareous mudstone and has yielded an extensive shelly fauna. Fossiliferous yellowish grey limestone is exposed in an old quarry [47219541] close to fault F1. The beds here dip E. at about 30° and contain the brachiopods '*Camarotoechia*' *nucula, Isorthis orbicularis* (J. de C. Sowerby), *Protochonetes ludloviensis* Muir-Wood and *Sphaerirhynchia wilsoni* (J. Sowerby) and the graptolite *Monograptus* cf. *leintwardinensis* Lapworth. South-west of Botvyle the outcrop of the Group strikes E.–W. and there is a good section in and around some old quarries [47309580] showing about 120 ft of grey crystalline limestone, locally nodular and well-bedded with thin mudstone partings up to about 2 in thick. In this area the limestone dips S. at about 75°.

UPPER LUDLOW SHALES

The Upper Ludlow Shales are thought to occur in the ground immediately S. of the quarries [47309580] in the Aymestry Group. There are now no exposures of these rocks but Cobbold (1900, p. 44) recorded the occurrence of fossiliferous sandy calcareous beds in this area which he supposed to represent the Upper Ludlow Shales.

7/CARBONIFEROUS

Carboniferous rocks occur in the N.E. corner of the area between The Lawley and Leebotwood, extending as far south as the neighbourhood of Botvyle [474962]. The rocks are part of the Coed-yr-Allt Beds of Upper Coal Measures age and consist of sandstones, siltstones and mudstones with three thin coal seams and their associated seatearths and also a band of *Spirorbis* limestone. The outcrop forms an area of low ground between the Uriconian ridge on the E. side and the Longmyndian rocks to the W. and is almost completely covered by drift deposits. It is probably limited to the S.E. by faults of the Church Stretton Complex and to the W. by a fault trending about N.–S. from near The Fields [474997] to near Botvyle [474962]. Because of the extensive drift cover there are no exposures, and our knowledge of these rocks comes mainly from old records of mining and from a borehole [47359653] put down for the Geological Survey near Botvyle. An outcrop in a stream [46949788] N. of Lower Wood, described by Whitehead (*in* Pocock and others 1938, p. 151) as Coal Measures, has been re-examined and is now considered to be Longmyndian, possibly part of the Burway Group.

Whitehead (*in* Pocock and others 1938, p. 150) described the Leebotwood area which lies at the S. end of the Shrewsbury Coalfields. Mining was carried on around the village until about 1876 and working was active in the time of Murchison (1839, p. 94) who mentioned the burning of limestone obtained from the mines in addition to coal. There are traces of old shafts N.E. of The Fields [47709990 and 48099998], at Hollyhurst [48169726] and N.W. of Botvyle [47479649]. Dumps of shale and sandstone remain around the shaft sites near The Fields where formerly there were also limekilns and brick pits. This site is shown on the Old Series Geological Map (61 S.W.) as the "Le Botwood

Lime and Coal Works".

A section obtained by D. H. Williams of the Geological Survey between 1841 and 1845 is thought to refer to one of the old pits near The Fields. A summary of this record reads as follows:

	Thickness		Depth	
	ft	in	ft	in
Drift deposits	26	0	26	0
Sandstone, mudstone and siltstone . .	67	0	93	0
Limestone	4	0	97	0
Sandstone and mudstone	30	0	127	0
Yard Coal	3	0	130	0
Sandstone and mudstone	24	5	154	5
Coal	0	7	155	0
Mainly sandstone	30	9	185	9
Deep Coal	1	3	187	0
Sandstone and mudstone	7	0	194	0
Red and blue marly shales to base at . .			200	10

According to information obtained by T. C. Cantrill (Pocock and others 1938, p. 151) in 1894, the pits in the area E. of the Shrewsbury road probably reached the base of the Coal Measures at about 360 ft depth and encountered hard rock, possibly Longmyndian.

A Geological Survey borehole [47359653] N.W. of Botvyle was put down in 1961 in an attempt to prove the Carboniferous and underlying succession near the site of an old shaft. It found about 60 ft of Coal Measures but unfortunately encountered a fault at 96 ft depth and thereafter entered Wenlock Shales; a summary of this borehole is given in Greig and others (1968, p. 257).

8/STRUCTURE

The dominant structural feature of the area is the Church
Stretton Fault Complex or Eastern Uriconian Axis (Pocock
and others 1938, p. 169), which trends N.E.–S.W. along the
E. side of the Church Stretton valley. To the N.W. is the
large outcrop of Longmyndian rocks which in the N. is
separated from the Eastern Uriconian Axis by the southern
tip of the Leebotwood Basin. South-east of the Axis are the
relatively simple areas of easterly-dipping Ordovician and
Silurian rocks.

Eastern Uriconian Axis

This includes the Uriconian outcrops of the Hope Bowdler
area and the Church Stretton Fault Complex which affects
rocks ranging in age from Uriconian to Upper Carboniferous.
The development of the structures within the Complex
has probably been controlled by movements along three
major faults, F1 (Church Stretton Fault), F2 (Lawley Fault)
and F3 (Cwms–Hoar Edge Fault), described by Cobbold
(1927, p. 565). Movements along these faults appear to have
taken place from Longmyndian times onwards. F1 extends
along the W. side of the Uriconian hills and forms a prominent
feature over most of its length. It has been described as a
normal fault with a westerly downthrow but estimates of the
amount of throw vary considerably according to the place
where the displacement is measured. In view of these
differences it seems probable that the fault movements
occurred at different periods and were not always in the same
sense or direction. South-west of Hazler Hill [468931] F2
and F3 are coincident and form the eastern boundary of
Ragleth Hill. To the N.E., F2 forms the E. limit of the
Uriconian rocks of Caer Caradoc, Little Caradoc and the
S. end of The Lawley. Because of the westward swing of

the fault in the Comley gap [485967] Cobbold deduced that it dipped W. at about 45° and described it as a reversed fault with easterly downthrow. F3 forms the N.W. boundary of the Uriconian of Hope Bowdler and Willstone hills and to the N.E. cuts Cambrian and Ordovician rocks. The fault plane is probably steep but the apparent throw is very variable and there is a change from a south-easterly to a north-westerly downthrow in the vicinity of Cwms Plantation [481947]. This reversal of throw may have been the result of horizontal displacement along the fault plane involving the development of the Sharpstones and Hill End thrusts [490945] and the lateral displacement of the outcrop of the Harnage Shales along the E. side of Ragleth Hill [452915 to 460924].

STRUCTURES IN THE URICONIAN

An important structural feature of the Uriconian outcrops is the apparent N.W.–S.E. trend of some fold axes. This can be seen on the map and geological section (Section 3) which shows a syncline developed in the Ragleth Tuffs and the underlying andesites and rhyolites. The thrusts mapped below the Cwms Rhyolites and Caer Caradoc Rhyolites may have been formed during this folding. A larger fold, with N.W.–S.E. axial trend, probably occurs on Hope Bowdler Hill [478933]. In this syncline a central core of Hope Batch Dacites is enveloped by the Woodgate Tuffs which in turn are flanked to N.E. and S.W. by outcrops of the Woodgate Batch Andesites and Dacites. The N.W.–S.E. trend of these folds contrasts strongly with the N.N.E.–S.S.W. strike of the Longmyndian rocks and may mean that the Uriconian was folded prior to the deposition of the Longmyndian. On the other hand Dr. Gilbert Wilson has pointed out (personal communication) that the Uriconian structures may be of purely local origin connected with the volcanoes which were active in Uriconian times and that they may have no regional tectonic significance.

STRUCTURES IN THE CAMBRIAN AND ORDOVICIAN

Cobbold (1927) recognized, in the faunal and sedimentary sequence of the Cambrian rocks, seven breaks of which six apparently resulted from uniform gentle uplift and erosion. The unconformity between the Lower and Middle Cambrian however, represents a period in which the Lower Cambrian was folded (Cobbold 1927, fig. 9), uplifted and eroded into an uneven surface on which the Middle Cambrian was deposited. This phase of folding has not been recognized in the Longmyndian or Uriconian outcrops and may have been confined to the Church Stretton Fault Complex. The present steep attitude of the greater part of the Cambrian rocks is probably due mainly to movements along the component faults of the Complex. The Cambrian outcrops are affected by numerous faults most of which penetrate the overlying Ordovician rocks. South-west of Robin's Tump however [48179530], a N.E.–S.W. fault between the Lower Comley Series and the *Orusia* Shales appears to run beneath an unconformable cover of Hoar Edge Grit. Similarly W. of Cwms Plantation [47669453] two small faults in the Lower and Upper Comley series apparently do not penetrate the overlying Hoar Edge Grit. This indicates a phase of minor earth movement in the period between the deposition of Upper Cambrian and Caradoc Series sediments.

The Ordovician rocks involved in the Church Stretton Fault Complex are steeply folded and faulted like the Cambrian largely as a result of movements within the Complex. In the vicinity of Cwms Plantation [479947] there is a syncline, with N.–S. axial trend, involving the Hoar Edge Grit and Harnage Shales and a small outlier of the Chatwall Flags, forming the core of the fold. This fold lies between F2 and F3 and is cut across by a subsidiary fault joining the two. The steep attitude of the Ordovician rocks E. of F3, to the N.E. of Willstone Hill may also be due in part to movement along that fault.

The Longmyndian area

The Longmyndian outcrop N.W. of the Church Stretton valley forms the eastern, normal, limb of the deep isoclinal syncline postulated by James (1956, fig. 4), and the core of this fold lies within the outcrop of the Bridges Group in the N.W. corner of the map. The Stretton Series, does not crop out on the W. limb of the fold, and James (1956, p. 333)

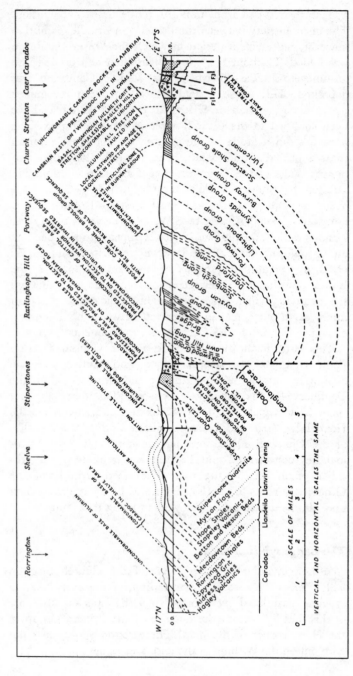

Fig. 1. *Diagrammatic composite section from Rorrington to Caer Caradoc to compare the inferred folding of the Longmyndian with folding of the Ordovician of the Shelve area and to illustrate various unconformities*

suggested that a downfold to a depth of about $3\frac{1}{2}$ miles on the surface of unconformity at the base of the Wentnor Series, would be required to account for this. His geological section, with minor modification, is incorporated in Figure 1 which shows the geological structure to a depth greater than has been possible in Section 1 on the map. There is a general pattern of steep north-westerly dips in the Longmyndian and the beds in the Stretton Series also young generally in this direction, but in the Burway Group [46669735, 46269678, 44809413] some beds dip S.E., indicating the presence of minor anticlinal folds superimposed on the limb of the major structure (see Section 1).

North-west of Church Stretton in the Habberley Brook area, shales of the Caradoc Series rest with strong unconformity on steeply-dipping Longmyndian rocks (Pocock and others 1938, p. 91, figs. 14 and 15) and it is thus inferred that the intense folding of the Longmyndian is at least of pre-Caradoc age. In the Shelve area W. of the Long Mynd there is a continuous stratigraphical sequence from Arenig to Caradoc Series with no evidence of contemporaneous folding. In the Cambrian rocks of the area small breaks in the fossil record and one minor phase of folding and faulting have been recognized but there is no indication of folding of such magnitude as has been proposed for the Longmyndian syncline. It is therefore suggested that the great Longmyndian downfold was formed in Pre-Cambrian times.

The Longmyndian rocks are cut by numerous dip faults of which the dominant trend is about W.N.W.–E.S.E., approximately normal to the regional strike. These faults cause lateral displacements of the steeply-dipping beds, commonly of the order of tens of feet but in some instances as much as 1200 ft. These displacements, both dextral and sinistral, are considered to result from mainly horizontal fault movements, since if the movements had been in a vertical sense, they would have had to be very large to displace steep beds by the amounts observed in the field. In addition to the dip faults there are four major dislocations which trend nearly N.–S. These include the Pock Fault (James 1956, p. 332) which trends S.S.W. from near Belmore Farm [408963], and along which there are exposures of hard grey silicified sandstone with abundant quartz veins, locally showing slickensided surfaces. The Long Mynd Scarp Fault was so named by James (1956, p. 331) and was earlier described as the West Longmynd Boundary Fault by Whittard (1932, p. 883), who remarked that there was no evidence of its persisting N. of Stanbatch [404937]. Within the area of the map the fault cuts rocks of the Bayston–Oakswood group and forms the E. limit of the low drift-covered ground W. of the Long Mynd. The Ashes Hollow Fault (James 1956, p. 332) trends S. from near the Boiling Well [423949] to the mouth of Minton Batch [420900] where it disappears below the basal Llandovery conglomerate. It does not form a topographic feature but can be delineated quite closely from the mapping of contrasting groups of the Longmyndian, on either side of the line along which there is thought to be a sinistral lateral displacement of about 4000 ft. The Yewtree Bank Fault trends about N.–S. through Yewtree Bank [408916] but is less well defined than the Ashes Hollow Fault. A sinistral displacement along this fault is used to explain the relatively close proximity of the Huckster and Darnford conglomerates near the head of Minton Batch [406920].

The age of the faulting in the Longmyndian was discussed by Whitehead (*in* Pocock and others 1938, p. 176) and Whittard (1952, p. 186). Whitehead pointed out that the faulting was probably later than the folding because of the nature of the fault displacements in the steeply-dipping sediments. Also a transverse fault in the Wentnor Series near Longden Manor (in the Shrewsbury district) probably, although not certainly, affected Caradoc shales. He concluded that the transverse faults were probably of late Ordovician (post-Caradoc) or early Silurian age. Whittard noted that the fault pattern in the Longmyndian is similar to that in the Shelve area where N.–S. tear faults are accompanied by a complementary set of shear faults. The Shelve faults were formed after the deposition of the Ordovician rocks and before that of the Upper Llandovery, so that the Longmyndian faults may be of the same age.

The Leebotwood Basin

In the Leebotwood Basin (Pocock and others 1938, p. 175)

Upper Coal Measures and Bunter rocks are downfaulted on the W. side of the Church Stretton Fault Complex. This indicates that movements occurred on the Eastern Uriconian Axis at least into Triassic times. Within the map, part of the Basin is represented by the outcrop of Coed-yr-Allt Beds in the Leebotwood area and little is known about its structure; however, from the scanty mining records there is no evidence of intense folding. F1 forms the E. limit of the Basin and it is bounded to the W. by a fault trending approximately N.-S., west of Leebotwood, which is thought to be the southern end of the Ercall Mill Fault of the Shrewsbury District.

9/GLACIAL, POST-GLACIAL AND RECENT DEPOSITS

The succession and distribution of superficial deposits is shown on the geological map. Glacial deposits occur north of the Long Mynd near Lower Stitt [403986], in the ground E. and W. of Leebotwood [476987], throughout the lower parts of the Church Stretton valley, on the lower ground N. of Cardington Hill [495950] and S.E. of Ticklerton [484908]. The deposits consist largely of boulder clay overlain locally by clayey gravel and sand and gravel. The depositional sequence in the area indicates only one period of glaciation, correlated with a maximum development of an ice sheet from the Irish Sea basin, which spread southwards across the Shropshire plain and around the high ground of the Church Stretton area. The deposits of sand and gravel which occur at various topographic levels are considered to mark halt stages in the northward retreat of the waning ice. There are also a number of striking river channels and dry valleys which were probably cut by melt water from the retreating glaciers.

Boulder Clay

In the vicinity of Lower Stitt [403986] there is an area of stony clay, shown on the map as boulder clay, occurring up to about 1100 ft O.D. Whitehead (*in* Pocock and others 1938, p. 197) suggested that the clay in the lower part of the valley might be of lacustrine origin. The stones in the clay include Longmyndian sediments, Stiperstones Quartzite and Llandovery sandstones, indicating that the deposit was probably laid down from ice which came from the Shelve area to the west. Between Picklescott [436994] and The Lawley [495975] the ground N. of the Long Mynd is largely covered by boulder clay which is locally overlain by clayey gravel, mapped as morainic drift, and by sand and gravel. West of Picklescott and Betchcott [436986] the boulder clay occurs at heights just about the 1000-ft contour, at which level it is also present between High Park [449970] and Jinlye [452962]. It is thought that the present margin of the boulder clay may represent fairly closely the limit to which the ice from the Shropshire plain overrode the northern slopes of the Long Mynd plateau. In the Church Stretton valley, boulder clay covers most of the ground below the 800-ft contour, and the occurrence of an area of boulder clay S.W. of Shootrough [490964] indicates that the Church Stretton glacier spilled eastwards through the gap between Little Caradoc and The Lawley.

The boulder clay is commonly brown but is rather varied in colour and texture and contains stones of local origin, granites carried by the ice from S.W. Scotland or the Lake District, and dolerite similar to that occurring in the Breidden Hills, about 15 miles to the N.W. of Church Stretton. Granite boulders have been found in the neighbourhood of Woolstaston at [44869850, 45139896 and 45949879], by the roadside 40 yd N. of Plush Hill cottage [45129642] and in 1963 were found in excavations for sewer trenches [440911], a short distance S. of Little Stretton village. Trial boreholes put down near the Betchcott Brook [456992] found up to about 50 ft of boulder clay and gravel in the Smethcott area (Whitehead *in* Pocock and others 1938, p. 194), and in the Church Stretton valley, a Geological Survey borehole at Springbank Farm [45719447] proved 80 ft of drift, composed of three layers of boulder clay interbedded with sand and gravel. The latter record may indicate three minor phases of advance and retreat of the valley glacier at Church Stretton.

Boulder clay occurs in the eastern part of the area between Cardington Hill and Folly Bank [497962] reaching to almost 1000 ft O.D. near the latter locality. This was probably deposited by ice which moved S. from the Shropshire plain around the E. side of The Lawley and which was diverted E. into the lower ground of Apedale by the Cardington hills. To the S.W. and S.E. of Ticklerton [484908] there is a thin deposit of boulder clay up to about 6 ft thick on the lower ground at about 600 ft O.D. and below. It is thought that this was deposited from ice which flowed eastwards through the Plowden gap [390870] around the S. end of the Long Mynd and which possibly met the ice, moving S. from the Shropshire plain, in the vicinity of Rushbury [513918]. There is no direct evidence however that the maxima of the northern and western ice were contemporaneous.

Morainic Drift

The geological map shows two small areas of morainic drift [500954, 500947], E. and S.E. of Willstone. These are parts of a larger area lying to the E. around the village of Cardington [506953]. The deposit is a clayey gravel of which the maximum known thickness is 26 ft, and which may be a terminal moraine deposited in front of the ice N. of Cardington Hill. Similar clayey gravel was separately mapped as morainic drift in the area between Picklescott [436994] and Leebotwood [476988]. Whitehead (*in* Pocock and others 1938, p. 194) noted that the drift of this area was stratified, consisting of impervious boulder clay forming the poorly-drained lower ground, locally covered by mounds of better-drained material. The lower parts of these mounds consisted of clayey gravel or stony loam, distinguished as morainic drift, which in some instances was overlain by bedded sand and gravel. Near Smethcott [450995] the sand and gravel appears to lie directly upon the boulder clay. Whitehead considered that the morainic drift was formed as a frontal moraine when the ice front lay north of the high ground of the Long Mynd. The sand and gravel was probably outwash material laid down upon the earlier deposits at a later stage in the retreat of the ice.

Sand and Gravel

The deposits of sand and gravel were laid down in the retreat stage of the glaciation; their relationship to the various stages of the retreat are discussed below in the section on glacial history. S.E. of Minton there are two small areas of sand and gravel [438906 and 437901] at about 700 ft O.D. A section in a gravel mound [43939054] showed 6 ft of sand with bands of gravel in which the pebbles were mainly of Longmyndian sediments but included one example of dolerite, very similar to the Breidden dolerite. East of Brockhurst Castle [448925] the Church Stretton valley is blocked by a ridge of gravel up to about 70 ft high. Just W. of the railway there is a large disused pit in which there are obscured sections in poorly sorted stony gravel, roughly-bedded at some horizons. Pebbles and cobbles from the gravel include quartz, local Longmyndian sediments, volcanic rocks possibly of Welsh origin, granite of Eskdale type, Uriconian rhyolite, and dolerite, similar to the Breidden dolerite. In 1959 the late Mr. T. H. Whitehead (personal communication) examined archaeological excavations in the inner ditch of Brockhurst Castle [44709254] and found 14 ft of gravel overlain by 2 ft of stony clay, possibly boulder clay. This suggests a minor readvance of the Church Stretton glacier subsequent to the deposition of the gravel.

On the N.W. side of Ragleth Hill at Plocks Coppice [462932] and Coles Wood [455927] there are deposits of poorly-bedded sand and gravel up to about 830 ft O.D. Pebbles found in the Coles Wood deposit include grits, quartz and one specimen of granite. In the valley between Hope Bowdler and Ticklerton there are three small areas of sand and gravel [476923, 479912 and 484908] which, it is thought, were deposited by glacial melt water which spilled eastwards from the Church Stretton valley through a col at Sandford Seat [468932].

Between Botvyle [477962] and Lower Wood [468976] there is a discontinuous gravel ridge which probably marks a halt stage in the glacial retreat. Near Cote House [469975] there are exposures of stony gravel with well-rounded pebbles in a sandy matrix.

The sand and gravel deposits of the Woolstaston–Leebotwood area have been mentioned above in the section on morainic drift. Whitehead (in Pocock and others 1938, p. 195) suggested that these gravels were laid down in a lake which occupied the low ground S. of the retreating ice sheet and from which the water escaped over a col in the neighbourhood of Church Stretton. No good topographical features apparently remain in the area to mark the original shore line of this lake. A large flat area N.W. of Leebotwood

[476988] at the junction of the Betchcott and Cound brooks is shown on the map as fluvio-glacial sand and gravel. Whitehead (*in* Pocock and others 1938, p. 200) noted that the surface of these deposits is nearly 450 ft O.D. in this area, but only 10–20 ft above the level of the recent alluvium. He considered that these deposits may have been laid down by melt water from the snow on the high ground to the S.W. and that, although they were younger than the other glacial deposits of the area, they were probably contemporaneous with boulder clay and outwash gravels of the Irish Sea ice sheet farther north. For this reason they were classed as fluvio-glacial gravels although they were not deposited by rivers issuing from an ice sheet.

Head Deposits

The head deposits shown on the map include two types which in some places grade laterally into each other. On the top of the Long Mynd there is a thick mantle of stony debris, derived by weathering of the solid rocks, which has moved little if at all from its place of formation. In the bottoms of valleys and on the more gentle slopes, deposits of head have accumulated by solifluxion processes, the material having been derived from the higher ground. The unmoved detritus on the Long Mynd plateau may have been formed largely by frost action during a glacial period when the Long Mynd was surrounded by ice on the lower ground. This frost weathering doubtless persisted on the Long Mynd in the Arctic climate which continued during the withdrawal of the ice from the district. The deposits of head on the low ground probably accumulated under the periglacial conditions which existed during and after the retreat of the valley glaciers from the Church Stretton area. No distinction has been made on the map between the solifluxion deposits of the valleys and the *in situ* stony detritus of the high ground.

There is generally very little head on the steeper slopes in the area, although in this connection an interesting comparison may be made between the north and south-facing slopes of the major Long Mynd valleys such as Ashes Hollow and the Cardingmill Valley. The north-facing slopes are mainly smooth and grass-covered with a thin veneer of rock debris and soil. In contrast the south-facing slopes show many more exposures of solid rock and, particularly along the outcrop of the Synalds Group, are locally rough and craggy. This difference appears to be the effect of insolation, particularly under periglacial conditions, which resulted in more extensive thawing and solifluxion on the south-facing slopes.

In the bottoms of many valleys there is commonly a deposit of stony debris which has accumulated partly by solifluxion but which has been reworked by the streams in the larger valleys to form narrow alluvial flats. These deposits are therefore mapped as alluvium, but in some of the larger dry valleys such as Cwmdale [452950] the cross section of the valley bottom is concave upwards and there is no development of an alluvial flat. In these instances the deposits have been mapped as head.

There are exposures in the head deposits of the Long Mynd plateau near Wildmoor Pool [42589656] and at [42549449] about 500 yd E. of the Boiling Well. These sections show up to about 7 ft of angular stony debris with no exposure of solid rock at the base.

Alluvium and Peat

In the Church Stretton valley the present watershed occurs at Church Stretton, the Cardingmill Valley stream flowing N. to the Cound Brook, while the Townbrook which runs to within 200 yd of the Cardingmill Valley, turns S. to Little Stretton. In many places these streams have developed small alluvial flats, but the dominant alluvial features of the main valley are the three delta fans occurring at the mouths of Ashes Hollow, the Cardingmill Valley and the Batch valley. The first two have spread right across the valley floor modifying the drainage. At Little Stretton the present southward drainage runs in a deep ditch cut through the fan beside the railway. It is evident that the accumulation of this fan caused the formation of a shallow lake or marsh which stretched from Little Stretton to Church Stretton around the W. side of Brockhurst Hill. Trench excavations for a sewer, dug across the flat [446922] S. of Brockhurst

Castle in 1963 and examined by the late Mr. T. H. White-head, found layers of clay, probably a lacustrine deposit, with beds of peat and peaty clay up to about 7 ft thick.

The Church Stretton delta has a very gentle convex surface with an indefinite margin and the present course of the Cardingmill stream is canalized across the fan in a straight ditch which is not its natural course. In a period of flood in the summer of 1957 the stream left the artificial channel and flowed via the site of the old Quarter Houses [455943] and to the south of Springbank Farm towards the railway. In its natural state the Cardingmill stream would probably have been braided across the fan so that the direction of flow might have changed from north to south or *vice versa* from time to time. Sewer trench excavations, examined by the late Mr. T. H. Whitehead, E. of the old Quarter Houses, [456942] showed grey clay, locally laminated and with scattered stones in other places, overlying and interbedded with angular stony gravel of the delta fan and with a 2 ft 6 in layer of peat. This sequence rests upon an irregular surface of boulder clay and Silurian mudstones. The peat and laminated clay indicate the former existence of a lake N. of Church Stretton and the sequence suggests that the fan gravels were built up by stages so that at the margins of the fan the gravels may interdigitate with the adjacent lacustrine deposits.

The delta fan at All Stretton is similar in form to the two described above but is less extensive and does not extend right across the valley.

The late Mr. T. H. Whitehead (personal communication) has suggested that the angular stony rubble of these delta fans would be more properly classed as solifluxion gravel which flowed out of the tributary valleys under periglacial conditions. This may be true of a great part of the material forming the deltas but they are shown as alluvial fans on the geological map, since they are continuous with the alluvial flats of the parent tributary valleys and it is likely that the upper layers of the fans have been reworked by stream action.

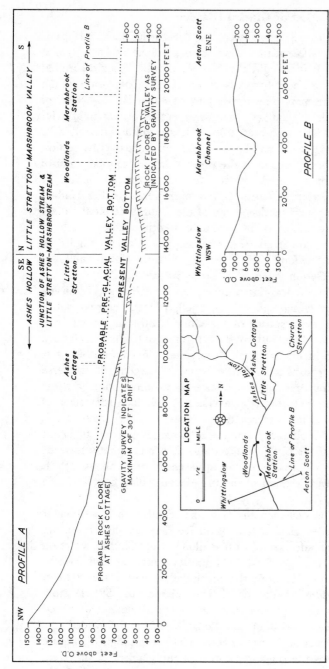

Fig. 2 A. *Longitudinal profile along Ashes Hollow and the Little Stretton–Marshbrook valley, comparing the present profile with the probable pre-glacial profile and showing the solid rock surface as indicated by gravity survey*

B. *Transverse profile across the Marshbrook valley from Whittingslow to Acton Scott*

Interpretation of Glacial History

In the Little Stretton area the pre-glacial land surface is preserved N.W. of the village as a platform at about 720 ft O.D. and it is thought that the main valley floor descended to a level of about 650 ft O.D. at Marshbrook, just S. of the area of the map. The upper part of Ashes Hollow N.W. of [428930] is of relatively mature aspect with narrow alluvial flats, and it is separated from a lower mature stretch S.E. of [435929], by a middle part with an incised cross section which is being eroded at the present day. The upper mature section appears to be graded to the pre-glacial surface at Little Stretton indicating that the erosion of Ashes Hollow was rejuvenated by deepening of the Church Stretton valley. This rejuvenation is also evident in other valleys such as Callow Hollow and the Cardingmill Valley. Figure 2 illustrates the longitudinal profile of Ashes Hollow and the Church Stretton valley S. of Little Stretton.

The Geophysical Department of the Geological Survey (Brooks *in* Greig and others, 1968, p. 312) carried out a detailed gravity survey of the Church Stretton valley from Marshbrook [442898] to Botvyle [477961]. The results are illustrated in Figure 3 which indicates a maximum of 155 ft of drift deposits near Little Stretton [44389163] (traverse no. 15) and only a small thickness, possibly about 30 ft, at Woodlands [44099069] (traverse no. 19). The rock floor of the valley appears to reach its highest level of about 520 ft O.D. at Woodlands, whence it descends sharply to about 450 ft O.D. at Little Stretton and then more gently towards the north. Thus there has apparently been about 270 ft of downward erosion of the pre-glacial valley floor at Little Stretton.

With the development of glacial conditions it is thought that a valley glacier, fed by an ice sheet in the Shropshire Plain, extended southwards along the Church Stretton valley at least as far as Hamperley [422892] and Marshbrook, while ice from the north-west invaded the head of the East Onny valley N. of Ratlinghope [403968]. Possibly at the same time ice from the Camlad valley advanced around the S. end of the Long Mynd and invaded the southern part of Ape Dale S. of Ticklerton [485908]. Figure 4 illustrates the suggested limits of the glaciers in the area.

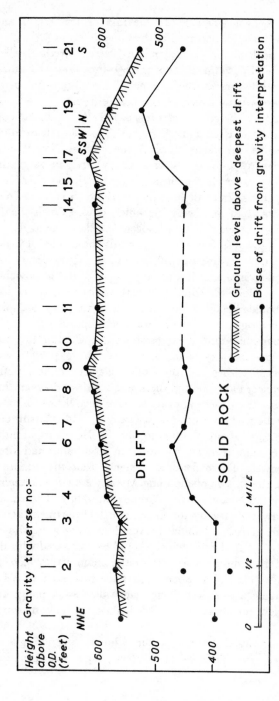

Fig. 3. *Longitudinal section along the Church Stretton valley*

79

It is not known whether the maxima of the Welsh and Shropshire Plain ice occurred at the same time.

At the peak of the glaciation the Church Stretton valley was occupied by ice up to about the 850-ft contour at Church Stretton, while the southern edge of the Shropshire plain ice sheet apparently overrode the northern end of the Long Mynd up to a height of about 1100 ft W. of Picklescott [435995] and at High Park [449970]. The Church Stretton glacier spilled eastwards through the gap at New House Farm [471943] into the Cwms valley and through the Comley gap towards Shootrough [491964], possibly surmounting the Chatwall Sandstone ridge S.W. of Folly Bank [497962] to join with ice which flowed down the E. side of The Lawley. This ice occupied the ground E. of Willstone [492953] but was apparently obstructed by the barrier of the Cardington hills to the S. No evidence has been found to indicate that the dip slopes of the Ordovician rocks S. of Hope Bowdler [475924] were covered by ice, and the boulder clay in the S.E. part of the map occupies only the lower ground of the Silurian outcrops.

It is suggested that the erosion of the Church Stretton valley below its pre-glacial level (see above p. 78) was largely accomplished by the valley glacier in its southward advance, but although there was 270 ft of downcutting at Little Stretton, there appears to have been little erosion of the ridge between Whittingslow [432890] and Marshbrook [442898] only about 1 mile to the S. Here, apparently, the glacier had reached its southern limit and had little erosive power. There is some evidence that the tributary valleys on the E. side of the Long Mynd were left as hanging valleys by the cutting down of the main valley. The results of a gravity traverse by the Geophysical Department across the mouth of Ashes Hollow [441920] indicate a maximum thickness of 30 ft of drift, which should be compared with the suggested maximum of 155 ft in the main valley 500 yd to the S.E. (Fig. 2). It appears that the rock floor of Ashes Hollow hangs above that of the main valley even though the land surface of these drift-filled hollows is now maturely graded.

The northward retreat of the Church Stretton glacier from the Whittingslow–Marshbrook ridge was probably

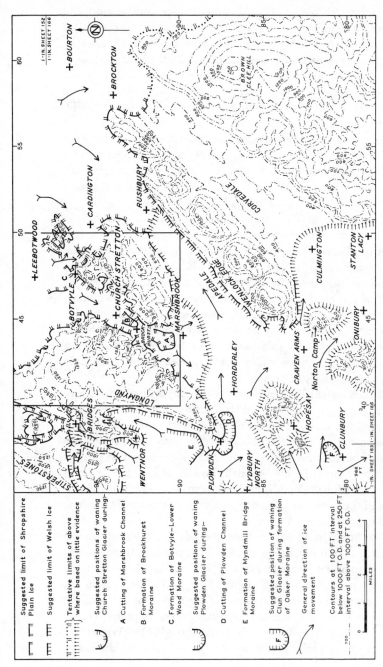

Fig. 4. *Suggested limits of glaciers in the Church Stretton district*

accompanied first by the deposition of spreads of sand and gravel [438906] by melt water from the glacier on the higher ground E. and W. of Marshbrook. The later channelling of the melt water into one stream resulted in the cutting of the narrow valley S. of Woodlands [441907] which carries the present southward drainage of the Marsh Brook. At an early stage in the retreat, on the N.W. side of Ragleth Hill, there was probably a marginal glacier lake at about 840 ft O.D. in which were deposited the gravels at Plocks Coppice [463932] and Coles Wood [455927], and which apparently spilled eastwards through the col at Sandford Seat [468932], the spill water depositing small spreads of sand and gravel at Hope Bowdler, Soudley and Ticklerton.

The gravel at Brockhurst Castle [448925] is probably a terminal moraine marking a halt in the northward retreat of the glacier. The late Mr. T. H. Whitehead (personal communication) suggested that when the glacier snout stood at this position, marginal melt water on the N.W. side of the glacier breached the spur connecting Brockhurst Hill to the Long Mynd and formed the striking channel W. of Brockhurst which carries the present southward drainage. The N.–S. part of this valley may have originated as a tributary to the main valley but its present form is probably due to erosion by melt water.

A Geological Survey borehole near Springbank Farm [45719447] proved 80 ft of drift, consisting of three layers of boulder clay interbedded with sand and gravel. The three separate layers of boulder clay may indicate minor phases of advance and retreat of the glacier, but at present however there is not enough known about the general sequence of drift deposits in the area to allow detailed correlation of the borehole sequence with divisions of the Pleistocene Period established in other areas.

The latest halt stage in the retreat of the glacier from the Church Stretton valley is marked by a discontinuous arcuate gravel moraine between Lower Wood [468976] and Botvyle [477962]. As mentioned above (p. 73) in the section on sand and gravel, the final phase of the retreat of ice from the area may be represented by the gravel deposits W. of Leebotwood [475987] which were thought by Whitehead to have been laid down in a lake formed between the ice to the N. and the high ground of the Long Mynd to the S.

Glacial drainage channels

North and west of All Stretton [460954] there are numerous dry valleys on the eastern slopes of the Long Mynd, occurring at various levels between about 1050 ft and 600 ft O.D. In some instances long spurs are cut through at several levels in an eastward-descending sequence. The courses of all these channels are shown on the geological map. It appears that they were cut by melt water issuing from the ice which stood at about 1100 ft in the High Park [449970]– Jinlye [452962] area. The occurrence of boulder clay in the lower parts of Gogbatch [462969] and the Batch valley [457955] indicates that the eastern valleys in the Long Mynd were occupied by ice, possibly lateral lobes from the Church Stretton glacier, or ice which had flowed down these valleys from the N.W. At an early stage in the retreat, melt water from the ice front at High Park would have flowed S. towards Church Stretton across the ice-filled valleys, cutting channels in the intervening spurs. With the northward retreat of the main valley glacier the ice in the tributary valleys would sink to progressively lower levels, allowing water from some of the channels to follow the courses of these partly vacated valleys down to the Church Stretton valley. For instance, in the case of the large dry valley of Cwmdale [452950] it is probable that melt water from the upper part of the Batch valley was diverted into the Cwmdale valley by ice standing immediately W. of All Stretton, to a height of about 900 ft O.D. The outflow from Cwmdale was past the site of the Church Stretton mineral water works [456947] into the main valley. This suggests that while the ice at All Stretton effectively blocked the mouth of the Batch valley, the level of the glacier had descended sufficiently half a mile to the S. to permit the egress of water from Cwmdale. A similar situation is inferred for the well-marked channel N. of Synalds Coppice. The upper end of this channel is near Woodnall cottage [458958] and at the time of its formation ice would have been banked against the steep slopes E. of Woodnall to a height of at least 820 ft O.D. It is likely that the outflow from the Woodnall channel was via the lower part of the Batch valley to All Stretton only ¼ mile S. of the ice barrier at Woodnall.

The Cwmdale channel is one of the largest in the area being about 100 ft deep at the highest point of the valley floor and about 200 ft deep at its lower end. It may not have been entirely excavated by melt water and possibly originated as a normal stream tributary or a nivation hollow which cut back towards the Batch valley. The later cutting through from the Batch valley with some deepening of the Cwmdale hollow is ascribed to the work of melt water. North of Worsley [455962] there is another striking channel which cuts through the spur between Jinlye and Gogbatch and then turns sharply S.S.W. following the 900 ft contour for 600 yd before descending into a valley at Worsley.

LIST OF REFERENCES

BANCROFT, B. B. 1928. The Harknessellinae. *Mem. Proc. Manch. Lit. Phil. Soc.*, **72,** 173–96.

—— 1929. Some new genera and species of Strophomenacea. from the Upper Ordovician of Shropshire. *Mem. Proc. Manch. Lit. Phil. Soc.*, **73,** 33–65.

—— 1933. *Correlation-tables of the stages Costonian-Onnian in England and Wales.* (Privately printed). Blakeney, Gloucestershire.

—— 1945. The Brachiopod Zonal Indices of the Stages Costonian to Onnian in Britain. *J. Palaeont.*, **19,** 181–252.

—— 1949. Upper Ordovician trilobites of zonal value in south-east Shropshire (ed. A. Lamont). *Proc. Roy. Soc.*, (B), **136,** 291–315.

BLYTH, F. G. H. 1944. Intrusive rocks of the Shelve Area, South Shropshire. *Quart. J. Geol. Soc.*, **94,** 169–204.

BULMAN, O. M. B. 1948. Some Shropshire Ordovician Graptolites. *Geol. Mag.*, **85,** 222–8.

CALLAWAY, C. 1874. On the Occurrence of a Tremadoc Area near the Wrekin in South Shropshire, with Description of a new Fauna [Abstract]. *Quart. J. Geol. Soc.*, **30,** 196.

—— 1877. On a new Area of Upper Cambrian Rocks in South Shropshire, with a Description of a new Fauna. *Quart. J. Geol. Soc.*, **33,** 652–72.

COBBOLD, E. S. 1892. The Silurian Outlier West of Caer Caradoc. *Midland Naturalist*, **15,** 217–21.

—— 1900. in *Church Stretton.* 1. ed. C. W. Campbell-Hyslop. Shrewsbury.

—— 1909–1933. Reports to the British Association for the Advancement of Science on excavations in the Comley area. *Rep. Brit. Assoc.*

—— 1910. On some small Trilobites from the Cambrian Rocks of Comley (Shropshire). *Quart. J. Geol. Soc.*, **66,** 19–50.

—— 1913. The Trilobite Fauna of the Comley Breccia-Bed (Shropshire). *Quart. J. Geol. Soc.*, **69,** 27–44.

—— 1921. The Cambrian Horizons of Comley (Shropshire) and their Brachiopoda, Pteropoda, Gasteropoda etc. *Quart. J. Geol. Soc.*, **76,** for 1920, 325–86.

—— 1927. The Stratigraphy and Geological Structure of the Cambrian Area of Comley (Shropshire). *Quart. J. Geol. Soc.*, **83,** 551–73.

—— 1931. Additional Fossils from the Cambrian Rocks of Comley, Shropshire, *Quart. J. Geol. Soc.*, **87,** 459–512.

1936. The Conchostraca of the Cambrian Area of Comley, Shropshire, with a note on a New Variety of *Atops reticulatus* Walcott. *Quart. J. Geol. Soc.*, **92,** 221–35.

and WHITTARD, W. F. 1935. The Helmeth Grits of the Caradoc Range, Church Stretton; their Bearing on Part of the Pre-Cambrian Succession of Shropshire. *Proc. Geol. Assoc.*, **46,** 348–59.

CREER, K. M. 1957. The Natural Remanent Magnetization of Certain Stable Rocks from Great Britain. *Phil. Trans. Roy. Soc.* (A), **250,** 111–29.

DAVIDSON, T. and MAW, G. 1881. Notes on the Physical Character and Thickness of the Upper Silurian Rocks of Shropshire with the Brachiopoda they contain grouped in Geological Horizons. *Geol. Mag.*, (2) **8,** 100–9.

DEAN, W. T. 1958. The Faunal Succession in the Caradoc Series of South Shropshire. *Bull. Brit. Mus. (Nat. Hist.) Geol.*, **3,** 191–231.

1960. The Ordovician Rocks of the Chatwall District, Shropshire. *Geol. Mag.*, **97,** 163–71.

1964. The geology of the Ordovician and adjacent strata in the southern Caradoc district of Shropshire. *Bull. Brit. Mus. (Nat. Hist.) Geol.*, **9,** 257–96.

DINELEY, D. L. 1960. Shropshire Geology: An outline of the tectonic history. *Field Studies*, **1,** 86–108.

GREIG, D. C. and WRIGHT, J. E. 1959. *in Sum. Prog. Geol. Surv.* for 1958, 30.

and others 1968. Geology of the country around Church Stretton, Craven Arms, Wenlock Edge and Brown Clee. *Mem. Geol. Surv.*

HOLLAND, C. H. and LAWSON, J. D. 1963. Facies patterns in the Ludlovian of Wales and the Welsh Borderland. *Lpool. Manchr. Geol. J.*, **3,** 269–88.

JAMES, J. H. 1952. Notes on the Relationship of the Uriconian and Longmyndian Rocks near Linley, Shropshire. *Proc. Geol. Assoc.*, **63,** 198–200.

1956. The Structure and Stratigraphy of part of the Pre-Cambrian Outcrop between Church Stretton and Linley, Shropshire. *Quart. J. Geol. Soc.*, **112,** 315–37.

LAPWORTH, C. 1888. On the discovery of the *Olenellus* Fauna in the Lower Cambrian Rocks of Britain. *Geol. Mag.* (3), **5,** 485.

1891. On *Olenellus callavei* and its Geological Relationships. *Geol. Mag.* (3) **8,** 529–36.

and WATTS, W. 1910. Geology in the Field, Shropshire. *Geol. Assoc. Jubilee Vol.*, 739–69.

MURCHISON, R. I. 1839. *The Silurian System*, Part I. London.

POCOCK, R. W. and others 1938. Shrewsbury District. *Mem. Geol. Surv.*

SALTER, J. W. 1856. On Fossil Remains in the Cambrian Rocks of the Longmynd and North Wales. *Quart. J. Geol. Soc.*, **12,** 246–51.

— 1857. On Annelide-Burrows and Surface-Markings from the Cambrian Rocks of the Longmynd. *Quart. J. Geol. Soc.*, **13,** 199–206.

— and AVELINE, W. T. 1854. On the Caradoc Sandstone of Shropshire. *Quart. J. Geol. Soc.*, **10,** 62–75.

STRACHAN, I., TEMPLE, J. and WILLIAMS, A. 1948. The Age of the Neptunian Dyke at Hazler Hill. *Geol. Mag.*, **85,** 276–8.

STUBBLEFIELD, C. J. 1930a. *in Sum. Prog. Geol. Surv.* for 1929, Pt. 1, 87–8.

— 1930b. A new Upper Cambrian Section in South Shropshire. *Sum. Prog. Geol. Surv.* for 1929, Pt. 2, 54–62.

— and BULMAN, O. M. B. 1927. The Shineton Shales of the Wrekin District; with notes on their development in other parts of Shropshire and Herefordshire. *Quart. J. Geol. Soc.*, **83,** 96–146.

WHITTARD, W. F. 1932. The Stratigraphy of the Valentian Rocks of Shropshire. The Longmynd-Shelve and Breidden Outcrops. *Quart. J. Geol. Soc.*, **88,** 859–902.

— 1952. A Geology of South Shropshire. *Proc. Geol. Assoc.*, **63,** 143–97.

— and others, 1953. Report of Summer Field Meeting in South Shropshire, 1953. *Proc. Geol. Assoc.*, **64,** 232–50.

In addition to the references listed above, a useful background to the geology of the Shropshire area may be obtained from:—

POCOCK, R. W. and WHITEHEAD, T..H. 1961. The Welsh Borderland. 2nd Edition (1961 reprint). *British Regional Geology. Geol. Surv.*

WHITTARD, W. F. Geology of some classic British areas: Geological itineraries for South Shropshire. *Geol. Assoc. Centenary Guide* No. 27.

Other publications dealing with this district

Books

British Regional Geology: The Welsh Borderland
Geology of the Country around Church Stretton, Craven Arms, Wenlock Edge and Brown Clee (Explanation of One-inch Geological Sheet 166, New Series)
The Geology of the Craven Arms area (Explanation of 1 : 25 000 Geological Sheet SO_{48})
The Geology of the Wenlock Edge area (Explanation of 1 : 25 000 Geological Sheet SO_{59})

Obtainable from the Government Bookshops in London (post orders from P.O. Box 276, SW8), Edinburgh, Manchester, Bristol, Birmingham and Belfast, or through booksellers.

Geological Maps

'Ten-mile' map of Great Britain (1 : 625 000)
Solid, South Sheet
Quaternary, South Sheet

One-inch to one mile (1 : 63 360) or 1 : 50 000
Church Stretton (166) Sheet, Solid
Church Stretton (166) Sheet, Drift

1 : 25 000
Church Stretton (SO_{49})
Craven Arms (SO_{48})
Wenlock Edge (SO_{59})

Tectonic Map of Great Britain and Northern Ireland (1 : 1 584 000)

Aeromagnetic Maps

'Ten-mile' map of Great Britain, Sheet 2 (1 : 625 000)

Obtainable from all Ordance Survey Agents

Diagram Edition, Sheet 5 (1 : 250 000)
English Midlands and Welsh Borders

Obtainable only from the Institute of Geological Sciences, Exhibition Road, London SW7 2DE

Printed in the UK for HMSO
Dd. 736183   C.50   8/83